RACHEL

AS Biology
UNIT 1

OCR

Module 2801: Biology Foundation

Richard Fosbery

Philip Allan Updates
Market Place
Deddington
Oxfordshire
OX15 0SE

tel: 01869 338652
fax: 01869 337590
e-mail: sales@philipallan.co.uk
www.philipallan.co.uk

© Philip Allan Updates 2002

ISBN-13: 978-0-86003-670-8
ISBN-10: 0-86003-670-7

This Guide has been written specifically to support students preparing for the OCR AS Biology Unit 1 examination. The content has been neither approved nor endorsed by OCR and remains the sole responsibility of the author.

Typeset by Good Imprint, East Grinstead
Printed by Information Press, Eynsham, Oxford

Environmental information
The paper on which this title is printed is sourced from managed, sustainable forests.

Contents

Introduction

■ ■ ■

Content Guidance

■ ■ ■

Questions and Answers

Introduction

About this guide

This Unit Guide is the first in a series of three, which cover the OCR AS Specification in Biology. It is intended to help you prepare for Unit 1, which examines the content of **Module 2801: Biology Foundation**. It is divided into three sections:

- **Introduction** — this gives advice on how to use the guide to help both your learning and revision and on how to prepare for the examination.
- **Content Guidance** — here you will find key facts, key concepts and links with other parts of the AS/A2 Biology course; you should find the links useful in your practical work and in preparing for other units.
- **Questions and Answers** — here there are questions on each of the seven sections in Module 2801, together with answers written by two candidates and examiner's comments.

This is not just a revision aid. This is a guide to the whole unit and you can use it throughout the 2 years of your course if you decide to go on to A2.

The Content Guidance section will help you to:

- organise your notes and check that you have highlighted the important points (key facts) — little 'chunks' of knowledge that you can remember
- check that you understand the links to practical work, since you need your knowledge of this unit when doing coursework or preparing for the practical examination
- understand how these little 'chunks' fit into the wider picture; this will help:
  - to support Modules 2802 and 2803 (you need knowledge of this module to be able to understand much of the content of the other two AS modules)
  - to support the A2 modules, if you decide to continue the course

The Question and Answer section will help you to:

- check the way examiners ask questions at AS level
- understand what the examiners' command terms mean
- interpret the question material, especially any data that the examiners give you
- write concisely and answer the questions that the examiners set

AS Biology

The diagram below shows you the three units that make up the AS course. You should have a copy of the specification for the whole course. Keep it in your file with your notes and refer to it constantly. You should know exactly which topics you have covered so far and how much more you have to do.

2801 Biology Foundation *30% of AS*	+	**2802** Human Health and Disease *30% of AS*	+	**2803** Transport/Experimental Skills Transport 2803/01 + Coursework 2803/02 *or* Practical Examination 2803/03
				20% of AS *20% of AS*

The specification outlines what you are expected to learn and do. The content of the specification is written as **learning outcomes**; these state what you should be able to do after studying and revising each topic. Some learning outcomes are very precise and cover just a small amount of factual information. Some are much broader. Do not think that any two learning outcomes will take exactly the same length of time to cover in class or during revision.

The unit test

The paper will be printed in a booklet, in which you will write all your answers. The paper will have six or seven questions, each divided into parts. These parts comprise several short-answer questions (no more than 4 or 5 marks each) and one question requiring an extended answer, for around 10 marks. In the extended-answer questions, 1 mark is awarded for quality of written communication (QWC). This is used to reward spelling, grammar, punctuation, legibility and organisation of ideas. The unit test offers a total of 60 marks and lasts 60 minutes.

Command terms

You need to know how to respond to the various command terms used in the unit test. These are outlined below.

'Describe' and 'explain'

These do not mean the same thing! 'Describe' means give a straightforward account. You may be asked to describe something on the paper, such as a graph. You may have to describe a structure or 'tell a story', for example by writing out the sequence of events in DNA replication. 'Explain' means give some *reasons* why something happens.

'Name', 'identify' and 'state'

These all require a very concise answer, maybe just one word, a phrase or a sentence.

'Calculate' and 'determine'

Expect to be tested on your numeracy skills! The examiner may ask you to calculate a percentage or the magnification of a drawing. 'Determine' means more than just calculate. For example, the examiner may ask you to find the percentage energy loss in an ecosystem from given data. This means that you have to select the appropriate numbers *and* do a calculation.

'Outline'

This means give several different points about the topic without concentrating on one or giving lots of detail.

'Draw', 'sketch' and 'complete'

'Draw' and 'sketch' mean draw something on the examination paper, such as a graph, a drawing or a diagram. 'Complete' means that there is something that you need to finish, such as a table, diagram or graph.

'Credit will be given for using the data'

This means that you should look at the figure or table given by the examiner and use some of the information in your answer. You may be able to do this by quoting from it directly or by identifying a trend and using the information to illustrate the trend you have described.

'Differences'

If you are asked to give some 'differences', then it is likely that you will be asked to say how 'A differs from B'. The examiners will assume that anything you write will be something about A that is not the same as for B. Sometimes the examiner will give you a table to complete to show differences.

Prepare yourself

Make sure that you have two or more blue or black pens, a couple of sharp pencils (preferably HB), a ruler, an eraser, a pencil sharpener, a watch and a calculator.

When told to start the paper, look through all the questions. Find the end of the last question (sometimes it is on the back page and might be missed). Find and read the question that requires an extended answer. Some points may come to mind immediately — write them down before you forget.

There is no need to start by answering question 1, but the examiner will have set something quite straightforward to help calm your nerves. Look carefully at the number of marks available for each question. Do not write a lengthy answer if there are only 1 or 2 marks available. If you want to change an answer, then cross it out and rewrite the answer clearly. If you write an answer or continue an answer somewhere other than on the allotted lines, then indicate clearly where this is.

When you reach the question that requires an extended answer:

- plan out what you intend to write and make sure you have a logical sequence of facts and ideas
- do not write out the question
- keep to the point — you do not need an introduction or a summary
- use diagrams if they help your answer — remember to label and annotate them
- pay careful attention to spelling, punctuation and grammar

Time yourself. Work out where you expect to be after 30 minutes (half-time). Leave yourself at least 5 minutes to check your paper to make sure you have attempted all the questions and have left nothing out. The best way to do this is to check the mark allocation — have you offered something for each mark?

Content Guidance

This Content Guidance section is a guide to the content of Module 2801: Biology Foundation. The main areas of this module are:

- Cell structure
- Biological molecules
- Enzymes
- Cell membranes and transport
- Genetic control of protein structure and function
- Nuclear division
- Energy and ecosystems

This section will help you to organise your notes and highlight the important points. The 'key facts' are presented as easy-to-remember chunks of knowledge.

This section will also help you to understand the links with practical work. You need knowledge of this module when doing coursework or preparing for the practical examination.

Finally, it will help you to understand how the key facts fit into the wider picture of biology — you need knowledge of this module to understand much of the content of the other AS modules. Module 2801 also supports those in the A2 course.

Cell structure

Microscopy

Key concepts you must understand

Size matters

It is very difficult to imagine the range of sizes that biologists deal with. A blue whale can be as long as 30 m. The largest viruses are about 0.0004 mm. Many plant and animal cells are between 0.02 mm and 0.04 mm.

We use microscopes in biology because much of what we want to see is so small. Many cells, for example, are about 0.02 mm across. At best, our eyes can only make out things that are about 0.1 mm in size, so using our eyes alone we would never see structures inside cells. The light microscope (LM) uses a beam of light that is focused by means of glass lenses. The electron microscope (EM) uses a beam of electrons focused by magnetic lenses.

Units

The units to use for measuring microscopic structures are the micrometre (μm) and the nanometre (nm). Remember:

- to convert millimetres to micrometres, multiply by 1000
- to convert micrometres to nanometres, multiply by 1000

Also remember:

- 1 μm (micrometre) = 0.001 mm; 1000 μm = 1 mm
- 1 nm (nanometre) = 0.001 μm; 1000 nm = 1 μm

Key facts you must know

Resolution is the ability to see detail. The light microscope has a resolution of 0.0002 mm. This means that two points this distance apart are viewed as separate objects. Visible light has a wavelength of between 400 nm and 700 nm. Objects about half the size of the wavelength interrupt the rays of light and are resolved in the LM. However, anything smaller than 0.0002 mm is not visible because it is too small to interrupt the light. No matter how much a photograph taken through the LM is enlarged, small cellular structures are never visible.

Magnification is the ratio between the actual size of an object and the size of an image, such as a photograph or a drawing.

Examiners may ask you to calculate magnifications or actual sizes. You should use these formulae:

$$\text{magnification} = \text{size of image}/\text{actual size}$$
$$\text{actual size} = \text{size of image}/\text{magnification}$$

With the light microscope, some structures, such as mitochondria, are just visible.

Electron microscopes
The wavelength of an electron beam is about 1 nm, so objects half this size are visible. As the resolution is so good, the magnification can be very high (250 000 or more). In the EM, magnets focus beams of electrons and an image is formed when the electrons strike a fluorescent screen or photographic paper. The **transmission electron microscope (TEM)** is used to view thin sections of tissues. The **scanning electron microscope (SEM)** is used to view surfaces of three-dimensional objects, such as the bodies of insects and surfaces of cells.

Inside electron microscopes is a vacuum. This allows electrons to travel towards the specimen and strike a fluorescent screen or photographic paper. It means, however, that living cells cannot be observed, since these would explode. In the light microscope, it is possible to watch living processes, such as cell division.

The following table compares the main characteristics of light and electron microscopes.

Characteristic	Light microscope	Electron microscope
Wavelength	400–700 nm	1.0 nm
Resolution	200 nm	0.5 nm
Useful magnification	×1000 (at best ×1500)	×250 000 (or more)

Links You may be asked to find the actual size of a cell or organelle in an electron micrograph or in a drawing made from an electron micrograph. Measure in millimetres and then divide by the given magnification. Multiply by 1000 to give an answer in micrometres (µm). You may also be asked to calculate the magnification of a cell or an organelle in an electron micrograph. You will be told the actual size in micrometres. Measure the size of the cell, convert into micrometres and then divide by the actual size. If you calculate a size, check it looks right. Here are some examples of things you may be asked: cells, 10–100 µm; chloroplasts, 3–10 µm; mitochondria, 1–3 µm; bacteria, 0.5–30 µm; membranes, 7–10 nm. If your answers are very different from these values, then you must have made a mistake!

Cell structure and function

Key facts you must know

Plant and animal cells have separate structures within them called organelles. Some organelles, such as the Golgi apparatus and endoplasmic reticulum (ER), are made from membranes; others, such as centrioles and cilia, are made from protein fibres.

Animal and plant cells are **eukaryotic** because they have a nucleus and organelles, such as chloroplasts and mitochondria.

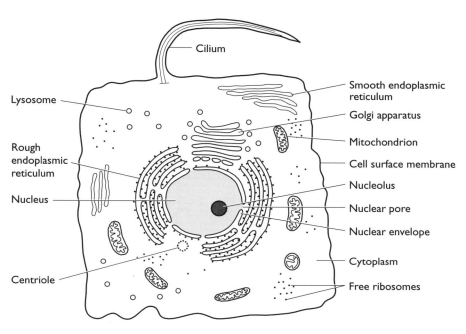

Figure 1 A generalised animal cell viewed with the electron microscope

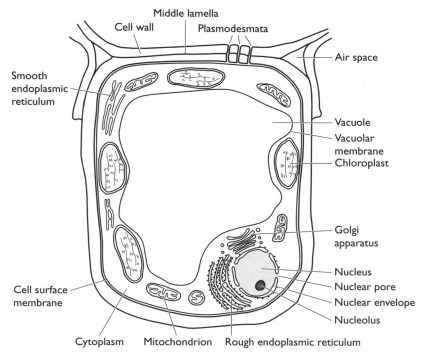

Figure 2 A generalised plant cell viewed with the electron microscope

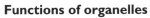

Functions of organelles

The following table summarises the features and functions of the main organelles in animal and plant cells.

Organelle	Features	Function(s)
Rough endoplasmic reticulum (RER)	Flat sacs of membrane enclosing fluid-filled space; outer surface is covered in ribosomes	Ribosomes carry out protein synthesis: RER transports proteins to Golgi apparatus
Smooth endoplastic reticulum (SER)	Like RER but with no ribosomes on outer surface	Makes triglycerides (fats), phospholipids, cholesterol
Golgi apparatus	Pile of flat sacs with vesicles forming around the edge	Modifies and packages proteins; makes lysosomes
Mitochondria (singular: mitochondrion)	Formed of two membranes surrounding a fluid-filled matrix; inner membrane is highly folded to give large surface area for enzymes	Site of aerobic respiration
Ribosomes	Attached to RER or free in cytoplasm — made of protein and RNA	Assemble amino acids to make proteins
Lysosomes	Single membrane surrounding fluid containing enzymes	Contain enzymes for destroying worn out parts of cell and for digesting food particles
Chloroplasts	Many internal membranes giving large surface area for chlorophyll, other pigments and enzymes	Site of all the reactions of photosynthesis
Plasma (cell surface) membrane	Several (see page 36 for details)	Controls entry and exit of materials, retains cell contents
Nuclear envelope	Structure like RER, with ribosomes on outer surface; pores to allow substances to pass between cytoplasm and nucleus	Separates nucleus from cytoplasm
Nucleus	Clearly visible in LM and EM when stained	Contains genetic information as DNA in chromosomes
Nucleolus	Darkly staining area in nucleus	Produces ribosomes
Centrioles	Made of protein fibres; structure similar to base of a cilium	Assemble the spindle to move chromosomes when nuclei divide
Cilia (singular: cilium)	Made of protein fibres; extend from cell surface; surrounded by plasma membrane	Move fluid or mucus past cells (e.g. in the trachea)

Key concepts you must understand

The cells depicted are 'generalised' cells. They do not exist! They are drawn to show all the structures in plant and animal cells. Sometimes you will be expected to identify organelles from electron micrographs or from drawings made from electron micrographs.

Links These aspects of cell structure and function will recur throughout the AS course. For example, in Module 2803/01 you will study red blood cells for transport in animals and phloem cells for transport in plants. In 2802 you will find goblet cells that secrete mucus and white blood cells that use lysosomes to digest bacteria.

Prokaryotes

Key facts you must know

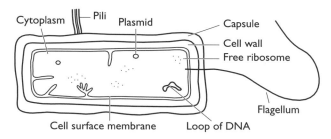

Figure 3 A 'generalised' prokaryotic cell

Prokaryotic cells do not have a nucleus and there are no organelles made of membranes. Most are smaller than eukaryotic cells. The table below summarises the differences and similarities between the two types of cell.

Structures shared with eukaryotic cells	Cytoplasm; ribosomes; cell surface membrane
Structures from eukaryotic cells never found in prokaryotic cells	Nucleus; nucleolus; nuclear envelope; mitochondria; Golgi apparatus; chloroplasts; cilia; vacuoles
Structures found only in prokaryotic cells	Ring of DNA (sometimes called bacterial chromosome)
Structures found in some prokaryotic cells	Small rings of DNA known as plasmids; pili (small projections from the surface); slimy outer capsule

Links Every time you come across cells of different types, check to see if they are eukaryotic or prokaryotic. When you study infectious diseases in 2802, you will find that the parasitic organism that causes malaria is eukaryotic; the organisms that cause tuberculosis and cholera are bacteria and are therefore prokaryotic.

Tissues and organs

Key concepts you must understand

Biologists often talk about **levels of organisation**. Organelles carry out different functions in cells. This is the cell level of organisation. At the tissue level, similar cells cooperate to perform one or several functions. In organs, different tissues work together to perform a variety of major functions.

Key facts you must know

Multicellular animals and plants are made up of large numbers of cells. Tissues are made of many cells that perform one or several functions. Often the cells are all of the same type. For example, epithelia are sheets of cells that line organs in the body and separate internal tissues from air, blood, food or waste that travel through tubes in the body. The outer part of your skin is an epithelium made of several layers of cells.

Animal tissues

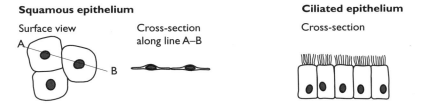

Squamous epithelium

Surface view

Cross-section along line A–B

Ciliated epithelium

Cross-section

Figure 4 Squamous epithelium and ciliated epithelium

Cells forming squamous epithelia are flat and very thin. Looked at from above, each cell resembles a fried egg, with the nucleus projecting like a yolk. Single layers of squamous epithelia, such as those lining the alveoli, are thin to help diffusion.

Ciliated epithelial cells, such as those lining the airways in the lungs, have many cilia to move a fluid or mucus over the surface. The cells have many mitochondria to provide energy for the cilia to beat.

Plant tissues

Xylem and phloem are the transport tissues of plants. Both are composed of three types of cell:
- cells that form tubes to provide a transport pathway
- parenchyma cells for storage and to provide energy
- fibres to help provide support

The transport cells in xylem are **vessel elements**. As these develop, they gain a strong, thickened cell wall and lose their cytoplasm, so becoming rigid and empty. They also lose their end walls so they form a continuous column of cells, known as a **xylem vessel**, which has little resistance to the flow of water.

The transport cells in phloem are **sieve tube elements**. These do not become thick walled and they keep some of their cytoplasm. The end walls are perforated to form sieve plates. They form continuous columns known as **sieve tubes** for the transport of soluble substances, such as sucrose and amino acids, throughout the plant.

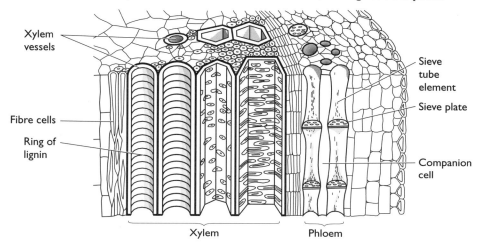

Figure 5 Transport pathways in a plant stem: xylem vessels and phloem sieve tubes in longitudinal section

Organs

The human body has a number of different organs, such as heart, lungs, stomach, pancreas, spleen, brain, kidneys and liver. Examples of plant organs are leaf, stem and root. Organs are structures made of several tissues that work together to carry out a number of functions. The leaf contains: epidermis for protection; parenchyma for photo-synthesis and storage; xylem for transport of water; phloem for transport of sucrose.

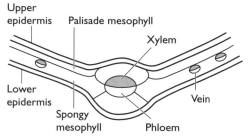

Figure 6 A plan diagram shows how tissues are distributed, as here in a leaf (note that cells are not drawn in plan diagrams)

Links You will meet squamous epithelia in the alveoli in this module (see page 40) and in Modules 2802 and 2803. Ciliated epithelia line the airways in the lungs and often occur with goblet cells — you will study them in Module 2802. The microscopy question in the practical examination may require you to recognise the four tissues mentioned here and write something about them.

Biological molecules

Tests for biological molecules

Key concepts you must understand

This learning outcome includes all the chemical tests for biological molecules that you should know. You may be examined on these in Unit 1 and in the practical examination. It will help your understanding if you know how and why these tests work. This is particularly important with the Benedict's test for reducing sugars, which is explained on page 17.

Key facts you must know

Test for starch
- Add a solution of iodine made up in potassium iodide to a test substance.
- If the solution changes colour from light yellow to blue-black, the test substance contains starch.

When describing this test, do not write 'iodine'; make sure you give it the full name — iodine in potassium iodide solution, or call it 'iodine solution'.

Test for reducing sugars
- Make up a solution in water of the substance to be tested in a test tube.
- Add Benedict's solution until there is a deep blue colour.
- Put the test tube into a boiling water bath and watch carefully to see any colour changes. Look out for green, orange or red.
- Leave to cool and look for a precipitate at the bottom of the tube.

If the test is positive, you will see a colour change and maybe some precipitate. This test gives a positive result with glucose, fructose, galactose, maltose, lactose and other reducing sugars. Sucrose solution gives a negative result. There is no colour change because sucrose is a non-reducing sugar.

Test for non-reducing sugars
You must first test your substance with Benedict's solution (see above) to find out if reducing sugar is present. If the result is negative, then you can carry out the rest of the test:
- Divide a solution of test substance into two samples (1 and 2).
- Add Benedict's solution to sample 1 and boil.
- If there is no colour change, add a few drops of dilute hydrochloric acid to sample 2 and boil.
- Cool and neutralise with sodium hydrogencarbonate.
- Add Benedict's solution and boil; if there is a colour change, the test substance is a non-reducing sugar.

Explanation of the Benedict's test

Reducing sugars act as reducing agents because they donate electrons. Benedict's solution is made by dissolving copper sulphate in an alkaline solution. The copper ions (Cu^{2+}) give it a blue colour. When heated with a sugar, such as glucose, the Cu^{2+} ions are reduced to Cu^+. A further reaction forms red copper oxide, which is insoluble and precipitates. If Benedict's solution is in excess, then the final colour is related to the glucose (or other reducing sugar) concentration. This is a semi-quantitative use of the test.

Sucrose is not a reducing sugar as it cannot donate electrons. It is a complex sugar made in plants by attaching glucose and fructose together. When sucrose is boiled with hydrochloric acid, it is broken down into these molecules, both of which are reducing sugars, which will give a positive result when boiled with Benedict's solution.

Test for lipids
- Add some alcohol to the test substance.
- Shake and allow the mixture to settle.
- Put some water in a test tube and then pour some of the mixture into the water.
- If a milky cloudiness is visible in the water, then the test is positive.

This is the emulsion test. Alcohol helps to disperse tiny particles of oil throughout the water, so making it opaque.

Test for proteins
- Make up a solution of the test substance.
- Add some dilute sodium hydroxide and dilute copper sulphate (either separately or together in a biuret solution).
- If the test is positive, a purple or lilac colour appears. If the solution goes blue, there is no protein present.

> **Links** The breakdown of sucrose is an example of hydrolysis (see page 19). These tests give opportunities for practical work and may form the basis of your coursework or a question on the practical examination.

Carbohydrates

Key concepts you must understand

Simple carbohydrates, such as glucose, can be joined together to form large molecules. Starch, cellulose and glycogen are polymers made of many molecules of glucose joined together. The three-dimensional structures of these large carbohydrates give them special properties and functions in cells.

Long-chain coiled molecules, such as starch and glycogen, are good for storage since they are compact. Amylopectin and glycogen are branched, which means there are plenty of places to add on glucose molecules when they are available and to detach them from when glucose is required for respiration.

Key facts you must know

Carbohydrates:
- contain hydrogen and oxygen in a ratio of 2 : 1, for example glucose, $C_6H_{12}O_6$
- have the general formula $C_x(H_2O)_y$
- include monosaccharides (e.g. glucose), disaccharides (e.g. sucrose) and poly-saccharides (e.g. starch (amylose and amylopectin), glycogen and cellulose)

Glucose molecules exist in two forms: alpha (α) and beta (β).

α-Glucose (note that the –H is above the –OH on carbon atom 1)   β-Glucose (note that the –OH is above the –H on carbon atom 1)

Figure 7

The difference between the two is very small, yet polymers formed when these two forms of glucose are joined together show important differences.

Two α-glucose molecules are joined together to form maltose:

glucose + glucose $\longrightarrow$ maltose

The glucose molecules are joined together by a glycosidic bond between carbon atom 1 on one glucose and carbon atom 4 on another. The bond is called a 1,4 glycosidic bond.

Glucose is joined with another simple sugar, fructose, to form sucrose:

glucose + fructose $\longrightarrow$ sucrose

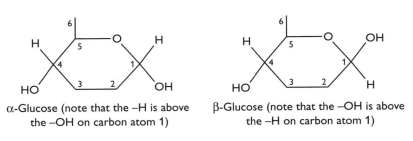

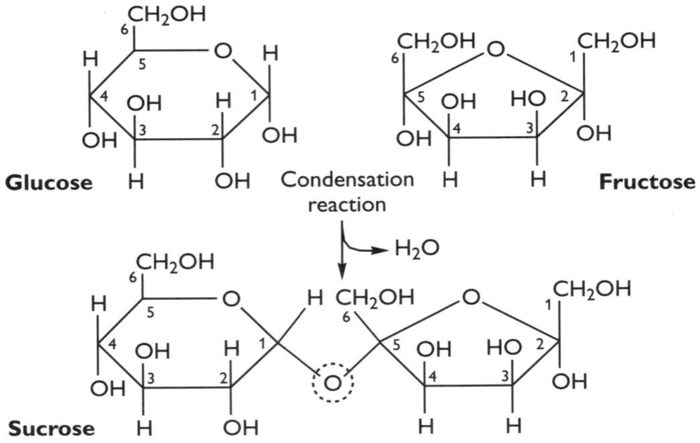

Figure 8 Forming a glycosidic bond between glucose and fructose to form sucrose

This is a condensation reaction, because a molecule of water is formed.

The following reaction is hydrolysis. It is what happens when sucrose (a non-reducing sugar) is boiled with hydrochloric acid.

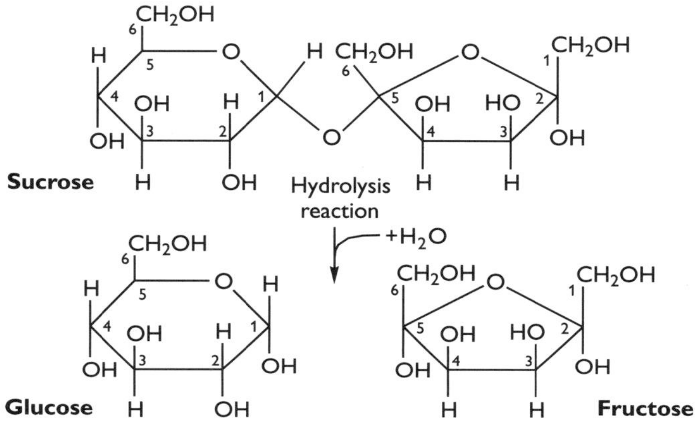

Figure 9 Breaking the glycosidic bond in sucrose to make glucose and fructose

The acid acts as a catalyst, speeding up the addition of water to break the glycosidic bond. Sucrose and maltose are disaccharides as they are composed of two simple sugar units joined together. Lactose (milk sugar) is another disaccharide; it is formed from galactose and glucose.

Starch (amylose and amylopectin), glycogen and cellulose are polymers of glucose. They are made of many glucose molecules joined by glycosidic bonds. Amylose is formed when α-glucose monomers, joined by 1,4 glycosidic links, form a long chain with a compact helix structure. Amylopectin and glycogen are also polymers of α-glucose, but some of the glucose molecules are attached by 1,6 glycosidic bonds.

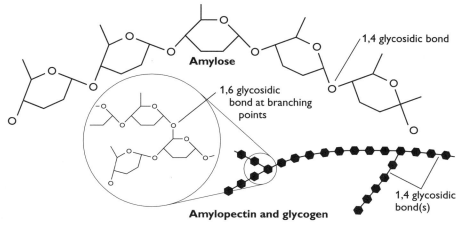

Figure 10 Branching points in amylopectin and glycogen are formed by 1,6 glycosidic bonds

Cellulose is a polymer of β-glucose. It consists of straight chains held together by many hydrogen bonds, forming rigid and tough structures. This is perfect for making cell walls which have to resist the pressures inside plant cells.

(There is more about hydrogen bonds on page 26.)

The table below summarises the main features of the four polysaccharides.

Polysaccharide	Monomer	Glycosidic bond(s)	Where found	Functions
Amylose	α-glucose	1,4 (unbalanced spiral molecule)	Starch grains in chloroplasts in plants	Energy store in plants
Amylopectin	α-glucose	1,4; 1,6 (branched molecule)	Starch grains in chloroplasts in plants	Energy store in plants
Glycogen	α-glucose	1,4; 1,6 (branched molecule)	Granules in animal cells, e.g. liver and muscle	Energy store in animals
Cellulose	β-glucose	1,4	Cell walls of plants	Structural — making cell walls in plants

Links When enzymes break down sucrose and starch, they catalyse the hydrolysis of glycosidic bonds. Page 31 shows you how to use the iodine in potassium iodide test to follow starch hydrolysis.

Lipids

Key concepts you must understand

Lipids are macromolecules. They are not polymers as they do not have repeating sub-units.

Key facts you must know

Lipids are a large, diverse group of compounds. Examples include triglycerides (fats and oils), phospholipids, steroids and waxes. Lipids are not soluble in water; they are soluble in organic solvents.

Like carbohydrates, lipids are composed of carbon, hydrogen and oxygen, but these elements are in different proportions. In lipids, there is far more hydrogen than oxygen. The major components of triglycerides (fats and oils) and phospholipids are fatty acids that have long hydrocarbon chains. The other main component is glycerol.

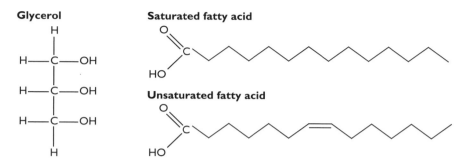

Figure 11** **Saturated fatty acids have no double bonds between the carbon atoms, while unsaturated fatty acids have one or more double bonds

Triglycerides

The fatty acids in a triglyceride can be the same as, or different from, each other. The bond that forms between a fatty acid and glycerol is an ester bond. During the formation of an ester bond, water is eliminated — another example of a condensation reaction.

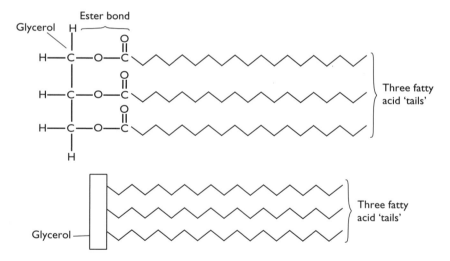

Figure 12** **Two ways of showing a triglyceride molecule

Triglycerides are not soluble in water. They are energy-rich and are therefore excellent for energy storage. When respired, the molecule is oxidised, releasing much energy and hydrogen atoms which form water with oxygen. This is metabolic water, which is important for desert animals, such as gerbils and camels. Fat is less dense than water, and so gives buoyancy to aquatic mammals, such as dolphins and whales. It is also a poor conductor of heat, so is an excellent thermal insulator. Its soft, cushioning effect makes it good for protecting organs, such as the kidneys.

Phospholipids

Phospholipids have a phosphate group attached to glycerol as well as two fatty acids. The phosphate is attached to nitrogen-containing, water-soluble groups. One of these is choline. This makes the 'head' of the molecule 'water loving' or **hydrophilic**. The two fatty acid chains do not 'like' water: they are **hydrophobic**.

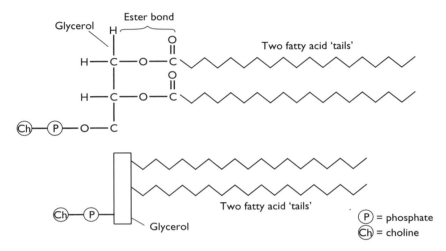

Figure 13 *Two ways of showing a phospholipid molecule*

Phospholipids form two layers (bilayers) to make membranes. They are ideal for this, as the hydrophilic regions interact with water in the cytoplasm and in fluid outside the cell, while the fatty acid chains form a hydrophobic core. This makes a barrier to the movement of substances in and out of cells as well as organelles made of membranes, such as mitochondria.

Links Lipase is the enzyme that digests triglycerides. You can follow the digestion of fat by lipase with a pH meter or indicator. This is possible because as fat is hydrolysed, fatty acids are released that lower the pH. This is a suitable practical for coursework or the practical examination. Fat in the diet is an important topic in Module 2802, since it provides much of our energy. The consumption of saturated fat is linked with coronary heart disease.

Amino acids and proteins

Key concepts you must understand

Proteins are unbranched macromolecules made of amino acids joined together by peptide bonds. Proteins are made from 20 different amino acids which can be arranged in many different sequences. This gives a huge variety of different proteins having many different functions.

Single chains of amino acids are polypeptides. These may be folded into complex three-dimensional (3D) shapes to form globular proteins, such as haemoglobin. Fibrous proteins, such as collagen, are made of polypeptides arranged in simpler shapes, such as helices.

Key facts you must know

Amino acids

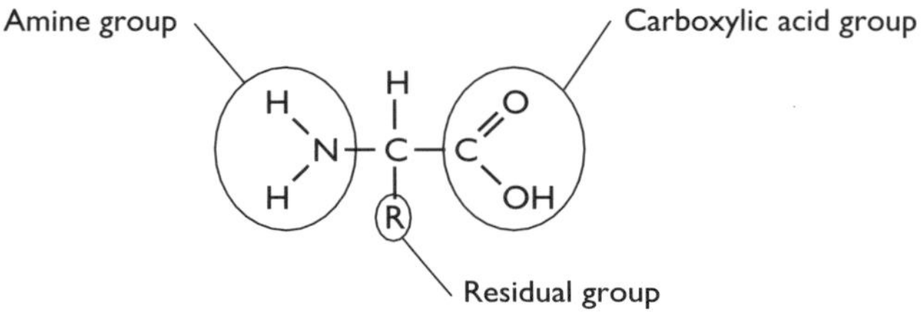

Amine group   Carboxylic acid group

Residual group

Figure 14 The generalised structure of an amino acid

It is the R groups that make amino acids different from one another. Glycine (the simplest amino acid) has hydrogen as its R group. Alanine has $-CH_3$. Amino acids are joined by condensation reactions to give peptide bonds.

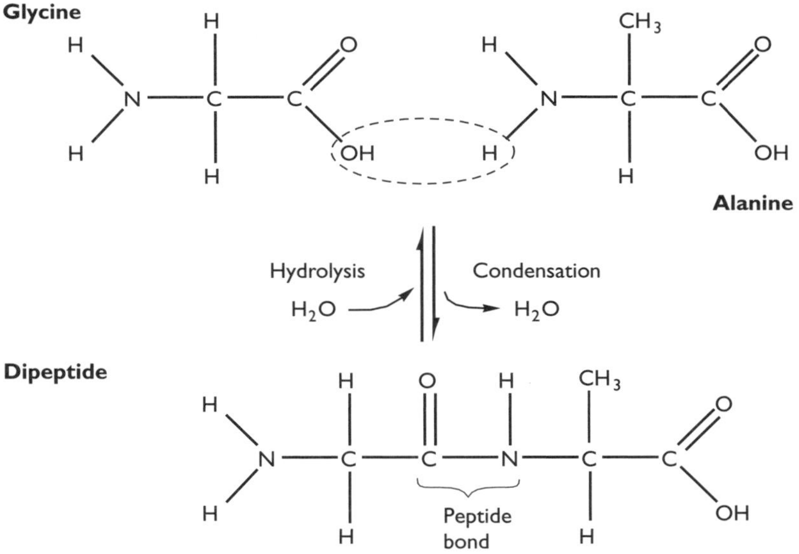

Glycine

Alanine

Hydrolysis   Condensation

H_2O H_2O

Dipeptide

Peptide bond

Figure 15 Formation and breakage of a peptide bond between glycine and alanine

Some proteins, such as the enzyme lipase, are made of one polypeptide; some are made of two or more. Haemoglobin, the enzyme catalase and many antibodies are

content guidance

made of four polypeptides. Levels of organisation in proteins refer to their structure. These are summarised in the following table and in Figure 16.

Level of organisation	Structure
Primary structure	The sequence of amino acids in a polypeptide
Secondary structure	Polypeptide folded into an α-helix (a right-handed helix), or a β-pleated sheet
Tertiary structure	Secondary structure folded to form complex 3D shape
Quaternary structure	Two or more polypeptides arranged together

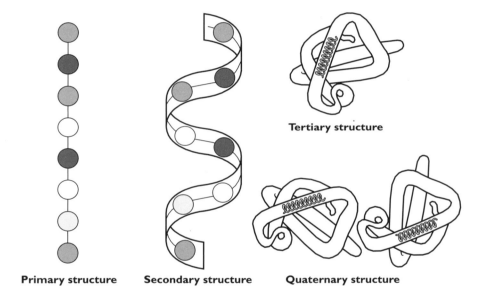

Tertiary structure

Primary structure   Secondary structure   Quaternary structure

Figure 16 Levels of organisation in proteins

Polypeptide chains are held in specific shapes by bonds that exist within the molecule (intramolecular bonds). Many of these bonds occur between the R groups that project from the central core of the molecule, formed by the carbon and nitrogen atoms (–CCNCCNCCNCCN– etc.).

Figure 17 shows these bonds.

The disulphide bond is the strongest of these because it is a covalent bond. It is formed between R groups of the amino acid cysteine. The R group is –SH and when proteins are formed, these groups react to form the –S–S– bond in the diagram. Disulphide bonds are useful for proteins, such as insulin, that leave cells and travel in the blood, as they help keep their shape. Ionic and hydrogen bonds break more easily, for example when a protein is heated above about 40°C or when it is exposed to a change in pH.

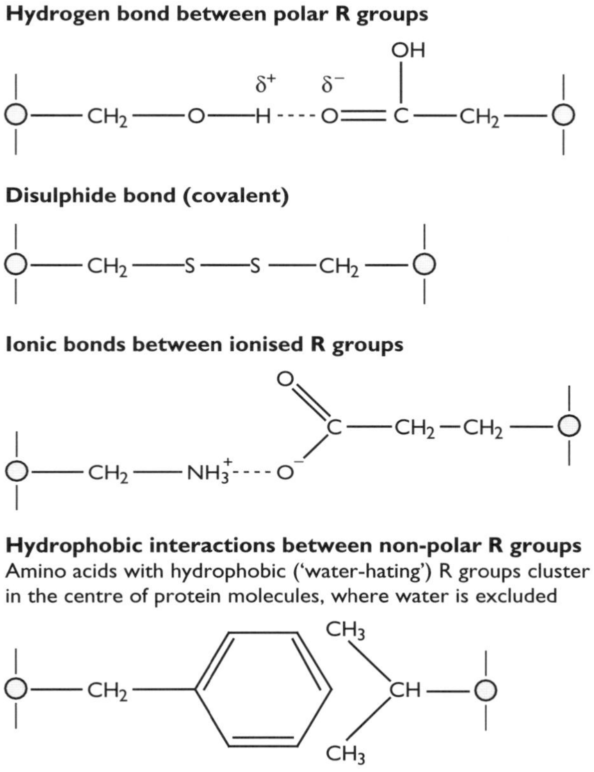
Hydrogen bond between polar R groups
OH
δ+
δ−
CH2
O
H
O
C
CH2
Disulphide bond (covalent)
CH2
S
S
CH2
Ionic bonds between ionised R groups
O
C
CH2
CH2
CH2
NH3+
O−
Hydrophobic interactions between non-polar R groups
Amino acids with hydrophobic ('water-hating') R groups cluster in the centre of protein molecules, where water is excluded
CH3
CH2
CH
CH3

Figure 17 Intramolecular bonds that stabilise proteins

Haemoglobin and collagen

Haemoglobin is a globular protein found in large quantities inside red blood cells. Each molecule of haemoglobin has four polypeptides: two α-polypeptides and two β-polypeptides. Each of the four polypeptides is attached to an iron-containing haem group. Oxygen attaches loosely to these haem groups to form oxyhaemoglobin.

Collagen is a fibrous protein. It is not soluble in water. Each collagen molecule is made of three identical polypeptides wound tightly round each other and held together by hydrogen bonds. The triple helices are joined together by covalent bonds to give very strong fibres found in skin, tendons and ligaments.

Links Genes determine the primary structure of polypeptides (see page 46). The specific function of an enzyme is determined by its tertiary structure. When most proteins are heated over 40°C, they lose this structure and are denatured. There are some enzymes that are not denatured until much higher temperatures, such as 80°C. These come from bacteria that live around hot springs. Knowing the structure of haemoglobin will help you to understand the way in which it works to transport oxygen. This is an important topic in Module 2803/01.

Water

Key concepts you must understand

We would expect water to be a gas at the temperatures on Earth. A heavier molecule with a similar formula, hydrogen sulphide (H_2S), is a gas. Most water is a liquid rather than a gas, because of hydrogen bonding.

Key facts you must know

Water molecules are dipolar (two poles). The electrons that form the covalent bond between hydrogen and oxygen tend to remain closer to the oxygen atom, giving it a slight negative charge (indicated by δ^-). The hydrogen atoms have a slight positive charge (δ^+), which means they are attracted to oxygen atoms on adjacent water molecules. This weak attraction between hydrogen and oxygen is called a hydrogen bond.

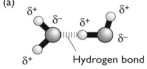 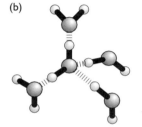

Figure 18 (a) A water molecule; (b) a cluster of water molecules held together by hydrogen bonds

Roles of water in organisms

Solvent action

Ions (e.g. sodium and chloride ions) and polar molecules (e.g. glucose and amino acids) are charged. They are attracted to water molecules because of the weak positive and negative 'poles' and are therefore dispersed easily in water, forming solutions. Water is a good solvent for ions and many biological molecules.

Cohesion

Hydrogen bonds cause water molecules to stick together. This makes it possible for them to travel up xylem vessels in plants in the transpiration stream.

Latent heat of vaporisation

It takes energy to break hydrogen bonds between water molecules and convert liquid water to water vapour. So, when water evaporates from plants and animals, it cools them down.

Specific heat capacity

Water absorbs a significant amount of energy before it changes state, so the temperature does not change quickly.

Water as an environment

Unlike air, water provides considerable support to organisms. Therefore, aquatic animals do not need strong skeletons. However, water is a dense medium and animals use energy moving through it. As the temperature of water stays fairly constant, organisms that live in water are not affected as much by changes in temperature as those that live on land. There is some oxygen dissolved in water, but air is far richer in oxygen. Some aquatic animals come to the surface to breathe, for example water boatmen and some pond snails.

Links Hydrogen bonds are important in stabilising proteins (see page 25), maintaining the structure of DNA and tRNA (see page 43) and forming strong molecules, such as cellulose and collagen. The transport of water in plants, which you will meet in Module 2803/01, relies on hydrogen bonding.

Inorganic ions

Key facts you must know

Ions are charged particles. Some, such as calcium, magnesium and chloride, are composed of a single element; others, such as nitrate and phosphate, are composed of two or more. Some of the biologically important ions are listed in the table below; there are links to topics in the AS and A2 course where you will study the roles of these ions in more detail.

Element	Ion	Function	Key links (module)
Calcium	Ca^{2+}	Helps transmit nerve impulses across gaps (synapses) between nerve cells Strengthens bones and teeth Plants make calcium pectate to stick cells together	Nerves (2804) Diet (2802)
Sodium	Na^+	Used in nerve impulses Maintains osmotic balance	Active transport (page 39) Diet (2802) Blood plasma (2803/01) Nerves (2804)
Potassium	K^+	Used in nerve impulses Used in mechanism to open and close guard cells around stomata	As for sodium
Magnesium	Mg^{2+}	Used in making bones and teeth Part of chlorophyll molecule	Chlorophyll structure (2804)
Chlorine	Cl^- (chloride)	Part of stomach acid (HCl) Maintains osmotic balance	Diet (2804) Blood plasma (2803/01)

Element	Ion	Function	Key links (module)
Nitrogen	NO_3^- (nitrate)	Plants use nitrate to make amino acids and nitrogenous bases	Nitrogen cycle (page 58) Amino acid synthesis (2804)
Phosphorus	PO_4^{3-} (phosphate)	Used to make phospholipids, ATP, nucleotides, tooth enamel, bone	DNA and RNA (page 42) ATP (2804)

Enzymes

What are enzymes and how do they work?

Key concepts you must understand

Enzymes catalyse chemical reactions. Without enzymes, these reactions would occur too slowly to support life as we know it. Reactions occur when molecules collide. Enzymes provide a place where reactions are likely to occur because they hold molecules under a strain, causing bonds to break and/or form. When molecules collide with enzymes in this way, they are described as successful collisions.

Key facts you must know

Enzymes:
- provide a site where molecules are brought together so that reactions occur more easily than elsewhere
- remain unchanged at the end of a reaction
- catalyse reactions in which compounds are built up
- catalyse reactions in which compounds are broken down
- change substrate molecules into product molecules

Enzymes are globular proteins with a tertiary structure held together by various bonds, such as ionic bonds. Different enzymes have different 3D shapes.

How enzymes work

The **active site** is the part of an enzyme where reactions occur. It is a cleft or depression on the surface of the molecule — a shape that fits around the substrate molecule. Therefore, enzymes and their substrates fit together like a **lock and key** to form an **enzyme–substrate complex**. When the reaction is over, the product (or products) leaves so that another substrate molecule can enter the active site.

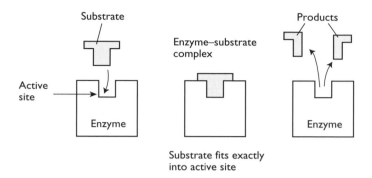

Figure 19 The lock-and-key mechanism of enzyme action

'Lock-and-key' is a simple model. There is evidence to show that the **induced fit** method, in which the enzyme's active site moulds around the substrate, is more likely.

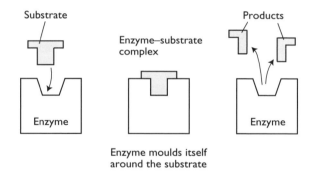

Figure 20 The induced fit mechanism of enzyme action

Each enzyme has a specific shape and usually only one type of substrate molecule fits the active site. Note that the substrate is not the same shape as the active site. It has a shape that fits into the active site, i.e. the two are complementary. Some enzymes are not as specific as others, having active sites that will accept a variety of substrate molecules with similar shapes.

Lowering of activation energy

Activation energy is the energy needed to break chemical bonds in reacting molecules. The reactions involve breaking and making strong covalent bonds and occur extremely slowly without enzymes because there is not enough energy to break the bonds and change substrate molecules to product molecules. Enzymes lower activation energy by providing active sites where reactions occur much more easily.

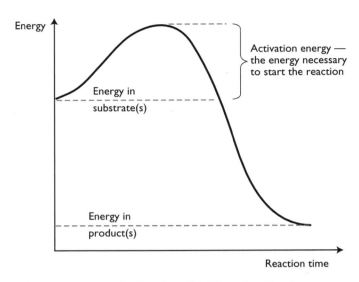

Figure 21 A graph showing the idea of activation energy

Enzyme molecules have specific shapes determined by their tertiary structure (see page 24). Some enzymes have a quaternary structure as well, since their molecules comprise two or more polypeptides. This means that some enzyme molecules have more than one active site. Catalase has four polypeptides and therefore has four active sites.

The tertiary structure of enzymes is altered by changes in pH and increases in temperature. As a result, active sites change shape and no longer accept substrate molecules.

> **Links** Many coursework experiments at AS involve enzymes. The practical examination may have an enzyme experiment. You need to have an understanding of what enzymes are and how they function to explain what happens in these experiments.

Following an enzyme-catalysed reaction

Hydrogen peroxide

Hydrogen peroxide is a toxic substance that is produced in organisms by several reactions. The enzyme **catalase** speeds up the breakdown of hydrogen peroxide to water and oxygen. Catalase is found in all sorts of things, from blood to sticks of celery.

This is the reaction that occurs:

$$2H_2O_2 \longrightarrow O_2 + 2H_2O$$
$$\text{hydrogen peroxide} \longrightarrow \text{oxygen} + \text{water}$$

The oxygen produced can be collected in a measuring cylinder by downward displacement of water or in a gas syringe.

The volume of oxygen collected is measured at intervals and plotted on a time–course graph. The course of the reaction is depicted by the curve on the graph.

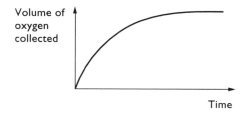

Figure 22

The volume increases until the reaction stops. No more product is made because all the hydrogen peroxide has been broken down.

Starch

Starch is hydrolysed into maltose because water breaks glycosidic bonds. It is a slow process, speeded up by amylase. To follow the course of the reaction, some amylase is added to a starch solution and samples from the reaction mixture are tested with iodine in potassium iodide solution in a spotting tile. At the beginning, the colour is blue-black. As the reaction proceeds, there is less and less starch and so the colour is lighter. Eventually, there is no colour change. At this point, the reaction is complete — all the starch has been changed into maltose.

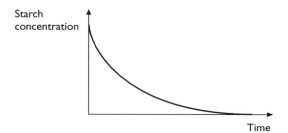

Figure 23

A description of these time–course graphs

The rate of these reactions changes with time. They are at their fastest to begin with, when there is the maximum concentration of substrate. They are at their slowest towards the end, when almost all of the substrate has been changed into product. When all the substrate has been used up, the reaction stops.

An explanation of these graphs

Rates of enzyme-catalysed reactions are determined by collisions between substrate and enzyme molecules. At the beginning, there are many collisions; later, there are fewer and fewer. The rate slows down because there is less and less substrate. The quantity of enzyme stays the same, but as time progresses there is less substrate to fit into the active sites available. The concentration of substrate begins to limit the reaction. The turnover number for an enzyme is the maximum number of substrate molecules that fit into the active site in a unit of time.

Links To investigate the effect of factors such as temperature and pH on enzyme activity, a number of time–course experiments need to be carried out and the initial rate of reaction found for each. The results are then plotted on a graph to show the effect of the factor investigated. Enzyme activity is often measured by finding the rate of reaction at the beginning of the time–course graph. You can do this by drawing a tangent on the graph.

Factors that influence enzyme activity

Key concepts you must understand

Enzymes are proteins. The active site is formed by folding of the protein (tertiary struc-ture). Denaturation is the loss of shape of the active site when bonds inside the molecule break at high temperature. Changes in pH also affect these bonds and cause them to break. Inhibitors fit into the folds and depressions in enzyme molecules, preventing them from working.

Key facts you must know

Temperature

Separate test tubes of starch solution and amylase are placed in a water bath at 10°C and left to reach temperature. Then the two are mixed together and samples taken at intervals are tested with iodine in potassium iodide solution, until there is no colour change. The time taken for the reaction to finish can be converted into a rate by calcu-lating 1/(time taken). This is then repeated for more temperatures (e.g. 0, 20, 30, 40, 50 and 60°C), and the results plotted on a graph (see Figure 24).

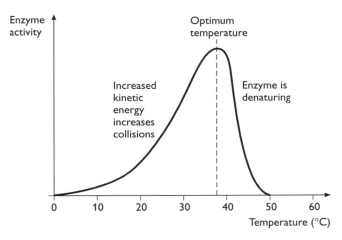

Figure 24 The effect of temperature on the rate of an enzyme-catalysed reaction

This is a *description* of the effect of temperature, as shown in Figure 24:
- Enzymes show no activity at freezing temperatures.
- Their activity increases as they are warmed from freezing.
- They are most active at their optimum temperature (human enzymes, 37°C).
- They are less active at temperatures below and above the optimum.
- There is no activity at high temperatures (e.g. above 50°C).

This is an *explanation* of these effects:
- At freezing temperatures there is no molecular movement, so no collisions occur.
- Enzymes are not denatured by freezing as they function on warming up.
- As temperature increases, substrate and enzyme molecules have more kinetic energy — more successful collisions occur between enzyme and substrate.
- At high temperatures, there is excessive movement within the enzyme molecules.
- Bonds (e.g. ionic and hydrogen) break, the active site changes shape and no longer accepts the substrate — the enzyme molecules are denatured.

pH

An investigation similar to the one described for temperature can be carried out for pH using different buffer solutions with the reaction mixtures. Buffer solutions maintain a constant pH. There are different buffer solutions available to give the range between pH 3 and pH 11, as shown in Figure 25, for example.

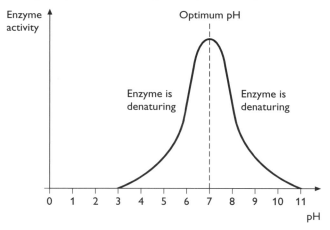

Figure 25 The effect of pH on an enzyme-catalysed reaction

This is a *description* of the effect of pH:
- The enzyme is most active at a certain pH — the optimum pH.
- It is less active either side of the optimum pH.
- It is inactive at extremes of pH.

This is an *explanation* of the effect of pH:
- pH is a measure of hydrogen ion concentration; as the pH of a solution changes, the charges on the R groups of amino acids change.

- At low pH, when the concentration of hydrogen ions is high, many of these ions interact with negatively charged R groups, so cancelling out their charge.
- This disrupts the ionic bonding between oppositely charged R groups within the tertiary structure — the enzyme shape changes.
- When active sites change shape, they cannot accept substrate molecules.

Substrate concentration

The effect of substrate concentration is investigated by setting up a series of test tubes, all with the same concentration of enzyme, but with different concentrations of substrate. The initial rate of reaction in each tube is determined and plotted on a graph.

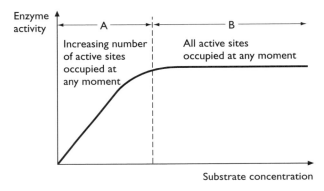

Figure 26 The effect of substrate concentration on enzyme activity

As the concentration of substrate is increased, the rate of reaction increases (see region A on the curve) because there are more substrate molecules for the enzymes to act on. Substrate concentration is the factor that **limits** the rate of reaction. At high concentrations of substrate (region B), all the active sites are filled and enzyme activity is limited by the enzyme concentration.

Enzyme concentration

The investigation is repeated with the substrate concentration kept constant and the enzyme concentration increased. The result is as shown below.

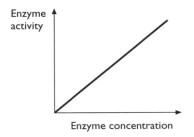

Figure 27 The effect of enzyme concentration on enzyme activity

With more enzyme molecules, there are more active sites available and so the only limiting factor is the enzyme concentration. This happens only if there are always plenty of substrate molecules; in other words, there is always an excess of substrate.

Inhibitors

Inhibitors slow down enzyme-catalysed reactions by fitting into sites on the enzyme.

Competitive inhibitors:
- fit into the active site
- have a shape similar to, but not the same as, the substrate
- block the substrate from entering the active site
- prevent the formation of enzyme–substrate complexes
- have an effect that can be reversed by adding more substrate

A good example is malonic acid, which fits into the active site of an enzyme in mitochondria that is involved in respiration. When malonic acid is added to a solution containing this enzyme and its substrate, the rate of reaction slows down.

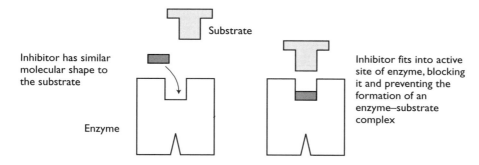

Figure 28 Competitive inhibitors fit into the active site and block it

Non-competitive inhibitors:
- do not fit into the active site
- fit into a site elsewhere on the enzyme
- cause the active site to change shape
- change the shape of the active site so it is no longer complementary in shape to the substrate
- have an effect that cannot be reversed by increasing the concentration of substrate

Non-competitive inhibitors are often substances produced by a series of chemical reactions inside cells. Each reaction is catalysed by a different enzyme. When there is enough product, it inhibits enzymes at the beginning of the process, so slowing down or stopping production.

The inhibitors described here are reversible. This means that when they leave the enzyme molecule, it can function again. You may read about irreversible inhibitors. They are not in the specification and you will not be asked about them.

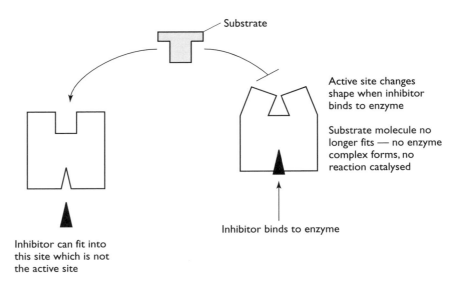

Substrate

Active site changes
shape when inhibitor
binds to enzyme

Substrate molecule no
longer fits — no enzyme
complex forms, no
reaction catalysed

Inhibitor binds to enzyme

Inhibitor can fit into
this site which is not
the active site

***Figure 29 Non-competitive inhibitors fit into another site
on the enzyme leading to a change in the active site***

Links Practical investigations for coursework or the practical examination may involve investigating the effect of a factor on the activity of an enzyme. Remember that all the other variables need to be kept constant. You are expected to explain how you would keep them constant, for example by using a buffer solution to keep pH constant.

Cell membranes and transport

Fluid mosaic structure of membranes

Key concepts you must understand

Membranes form boundaries and divide cells into compartments. The cell membrane (plasma membrane or cell surface membrane) forms the outermost boundary of the cell. This allows cells to be different from their external environment. Membranes keep in large molecules such as enzymes, RNA and DNA. They keep out many others. They are barriers between the cytoplasm and the outside world. But cells need to exchange substances with their surroundings, so membranes are permeable — not freely permeable to anything and everything but **partially permeable** to some substances.

Organelles, for example mitochondria, chloroplasts, endoplasmic reticulum and Golgi apparatus, are made of membranes and are separate compartments within cells. For example, the lysosome membrane encloses hydrolytic enzymes and stops them breaking down molecules, such as proteins, in the cytoplasm.

Key facts you must know

All membranes have the same basic structure — the fluid mosaic structure.

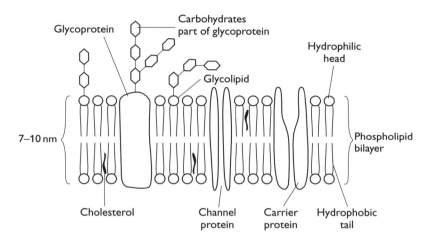

Figure 30 The fluid mosaic model of membrane structure

Figure 30 shows a cross-section of a tiny part of a membrane. It is composed of a double layer (bilayer) of phospholipids, together with proteins. Each phospholipid molecule has a 'head' and two 'tails'. The head end is polar and 'water-loving' (hydrophilic). The tails are non-polar and 'water-hating' (hydrophobic). Phospholipid heads are soluble in water; the tails provide a hydrophobic barrier that many water-soluble substances cannot cross easily. This hydrophobic barrier restricts the movement of substances in and out of cells, so helping to keep a constant environment inside the cytoplasm.

How are the components arranged?
Phospholipids
- Membranes have two layers of phospholipid, forming a bilayer.
- The molecules in the two layers have opposite orientations, so that the non-polar ends associate with each other and the polar ends face the cytoplasm and the fluid outside the cell.

Proteins
- Membrane proteins are embedded in the phospholipid bilayer. Transmembrane proteins extend right through the bilayer with one end in the cytoplasm and the other end extending to the outside.
- Transmembrane proteins are held in the membrane because they have hydrophobic regions that span the hydrophobic interior of the membrane.

Carbohydrates

- These are short chains of sugar molecules that branch to give 'tree-like' attachments to proteins and phospholipids.
- Glycolipids are phospholipids with chains of sugar molecules attached.
- Glycoproteins are proteins with chains of sugar molecules attached.
- Carbohydrates are attached to lipids and proteins only on the external surfaces of cell membranes.

Why fluid mosaic?

Fluid

The membrane is held together mainly by hydrophobic interactions between the phospholipids and between proteins and phospholipids. These weak interactions allow the molecules to move. Phospholipid molecules move in the plane of the membrane. Proteins are much larger and move more slowly — imagine protein molecules moving about like icebergs in a 'sea' of lipid.

Mosaic

A membrane is like a collage of many different proteins in the lipid bilayer. Think of a mosaic that is made of tiny pieces of tile. Now think of the pieces constantly moving about and you should have a picture in your mind of a fluid mosaic!

> **Links** Membranes are involved in all exchanges between living things and their environment, for example across alveoli and across plant root hairs (see page 41).

Movement across membranes

Key concepts you must understand

Membranes are barriers, but they allow considerable exchange of substances between the cytoplasm and the surroundings. Some substances are small enough to pass through membranes quite easily; others are larger and need special methods.

Key facts you must know

There are five ways in which substances can cross membranes:
- simple diffusion
- facilitated diffusion
- osmosis
- active transport
- bulk transport (endocytosis and exocytosis)

Simple diffusion

Non-polar molecules (such as steroid hormones, lipid-soluble vitamins and many narcotics) and very small, uncharged molecules (such as water, urea, oxygen and carbon dioxide) move through the phospholipid bilayer down their concentration gradients. This is a passive process. Larger molecules (such as sugars) and charged substances (such as inorganic ions) cannot diffuse across membranes in this way.

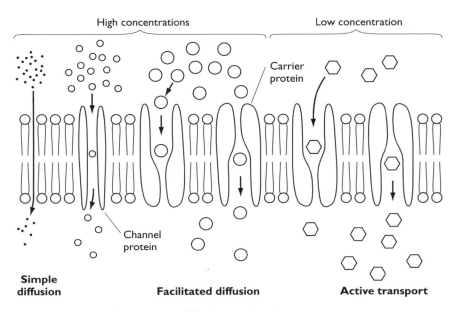

Figure 31 Diffusion and active transport

Facilitated diffusion

Proteins play a key role in regulating transport across membranes. **Channel proteins** each have a hollow core, which acts as a water-filled channel or pore. This allows small, polar molecules and ions to diffuse across membranes. This is known as facilitated diffusion as the channels allow this to happen (facilitated = make easier).

Carrier proteins work by binding onto the substance and physically moving it across. The binding causes a change in the shape of the carrier and results in the bound substance being released at the other side. This is also a type of facilitated diffusion when the substances involved move down their concentration gradients.

Osmosis

Osmosis is the diffusion of water across membranes. It diffuses through the phospholipids and channel proteins down a water potential gradient, which is determined partly by the solute concentration in the cytoplasm and the external surroundings and partly by other factors, for example the pressure exerted by plant cell walls on the cytoplasm and vacuole.

Active transport

Active transport involves carrier proteins. Cells use energy to move substances from a low to a high concentration (against a concentration gradient). Many cells use active transport to move sodium ions out of the cytoplasm in exchange for potassium ions — the 'sodium pump'. This helps regulate their volume, as three sodium ions are pumped out for every two potassium ions pumped in. Removing sodium ions helps to prevent the cell water potential falling very low and too much water diffusing in by osmosis.

Bulk transport

Bulk transport is used for the transport of larger molecules and particles. Exocytosis and endocytosis (pinocytosis and phagocytosis) are examples.

Exocytosis

Substances are moved out of cells. Vesicles travel towards the cell surface and fuse with the membrane to extrude substances. For example, this happens when cells in the stomach lining secrete enzymes into the gut.

Endocytosis

Substances are brought into cells. Vesicles form at the cell surface and move into the cell. For example, this happens when white blood cells 'eat' and digest bacteria.

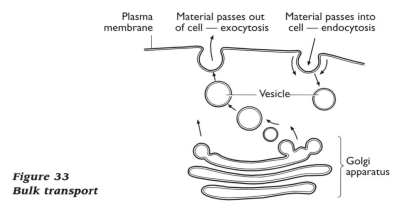

Figure 33
Bulk transport

Alveoli and root hairs

Key concepts you must understand

The alveoli in the lungs form a very large surface area. Roots grow many thousands of root hairs. Alveoli and root hairs provide very large surfaces for the uptake and exchange of substances. In the alveoli, gaseous exchange occurs as oxygen diffuses into the blood and carbon dioxide diffuses out.

Key facts you must know

Gaseous exchange in the alveolus

Alveoli are tiny air-filled sacs, adapted for exchange of gases by diffusion between the air and blood capillaries. There are two main ways in which alveoli are adapted.

Short diffusion distance

Cells lining alveoli and blood capillaries are thin, squamous, epithelial cells. This allows easy diffusion of oxygen and carbon dioxide even though there are five cell membranes between the air and the haemoglobin inside red blood cells.

Steep concentration gradient

Breathing ventilates the alveoli, maintaining a high concentration of oxygen in alveolar air; blood flows through capillaries in the lungs, bringing a constant supply of deoxygenated blood. The difference between the concentrations of oxygen in the air and the blood is called a concentration gradient. Breathing and the flow of blood maintain a large difference (or a steep concentration gradient), so that diffusion of oxygen from the air into the blood is rapid. Exactly the opposite happens with carbon dioxide, although the concentration gradient is not as steep. (You will discover the reasons for this when you study Module 2803/01.)

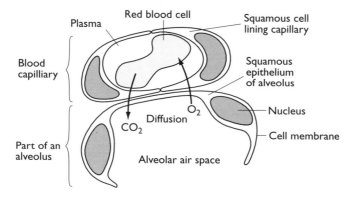

Figure 33 Features of the gaseous exchange surface in the lungs

Root hairs

Plants continually grow new roots. Near the end of each new root are many fine root hairs, which absorb water and ions from the soil. Water is absorbed by osmosis; ions are absorbed by diffusion or active transport. Ions present in soil water in lower concentrations than in root hair cells are absorbed by active transport. Absorption of ions lowers the water potential of root hair cytoplasm, so helping to absorb water by osmosis.

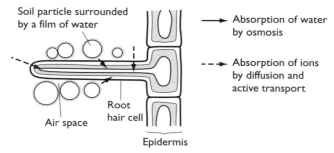

Figure 34 Root hairs are thin extensions of epidermal cells of young roots

Links It is likely that you will do some experiments on osmosis. You will need to explain your results in terms of water potential.

Genetic control of protein structure and function

DNA and RNA — the nucleic acids

Key concepts you must understand

Nucleic acids are for information storage and retrieval. DNA (deoxyribonucleic acid) is a large, very stable molecule found in chromosomes. It forms the genes that code for proteins. You inherited it from your parents and you will pass it on to your children. It is a long-term store of genetic information. RNA (ribonucleic acid) is a shorter molecule that cells use to retrieve information from DNA and express it in the form of proteins.

Key facts you must know

DNA and RNA are macromolecules made of repeating sub-units which are joined together by covalent bonds. Nucleotides are the sub-unit molecules of nucleic acids. Cells join these nucleotides together to form polynucleotides.

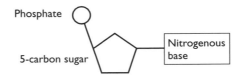

Figure 35 All nucleotides have this structure (the box represents one of five different nitrogenous bases)

The nucleotides that make up DNA contain the sugar deoxyribose; the nucleotides that make up RNA contain ribose. The different DNA and RNA nucleotides are shown in the table below. There are two types of base: purines and pyrimidines. Purine bases have two rings of carbon and nitrogen atoms; pyrimidines have one.

	Purines		Pyrimidines		
Number of rings	2		1		
Bases	Adenine	Guanine	Cytosine	Thymine	Uracil
DNA	✓	✓	✓	✓	✗
RNA	✓	✓	✓	✗	✓

In both DNA and RNA, there are four different bases, but thymine is found only in DNA and uracil is found only in RNA (i.e. in RNA, uracil replaces thymine).

All DNA (except some in viruses) is 'double-stranded'. This means that there are two 'strands', or polynucleotides, side by side. The bases on opposite strands are joined together by hydrogen bonds. These are not as strong as the covalent bonds joining adjacent nucleotides, but because there are so many it is quite difficult to break the strands apart. This helps to make DNA a very stable molecule.

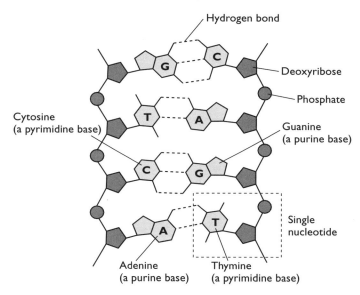

Note: Adenine (A) always bonds with thymine (T)
Guanine (G) always bonds with cytosine (C)

Figure 36 The molecular structure of DNA

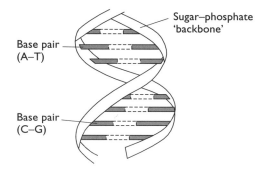

Figure 37 The two 'strands' are twisted around each other to form the famous DNA double helix (this shows a small part of the double helix of DNA)

Base pairing in DNA is always as follows:
- adenine to thymine (A–T)
- guanine to cytosine (G–C)

There are three types of RNA:

Type of RNA	Function
Messenger RNA (mRNA)	Takes copies of genes from DNA in nucleus to ribosomes
Ribosomal RNA (rRNA)	Helps make sites in ribosomes for assembling proteins from amino acids
Transfer RNA (tRNA)	Carries amino acids to ribosomes; anticodon identifes each amino acid

Molecules of RNA are 'single-stranded' polynucleotides. There are hydrogen bonds between some base pairs in tRNA to give a 'cloverleaf' shape. There are no hydrogen bonds in mRNA: it is a single, unfolded chain. DNA and messenger RNA are compared below.

Feature	DNA	Messenger RNA
Overall structure	Double helix	Single chain
Overall size of molecule	Very large	Small
Name of pentose (5C) sugar	Deoxyribose	Ribose
Number of polynucleotide chains	2	1
Nitrogenous bases	Adenine (A), thymine (T), cytosine (C) and guanine (G)	Adenine (A), uracil (U), cytosine (C) and guanine (G)
Base pairing	A pairs with T (A–T) C pairs with G (C–G)	No base pairing
Function	Long-term storage of genetic information	Transfer of genetic information from nucleus to ribosomes
Where found in eukaryotic cells	Nucleus; also some in mitochondria and chloroplasts	Nucleus and cytoplasm; also attached to ribosomes during translation (see page 48)

Replication

Key concepts you must understand

DNA replication is DNA copying itself. Cells provide nucleotides, energy and enzymes for the process, but the important point is that DNA acts as a **template** so that new polynucleotide chains are built up on already existing ones. This is called **semi-conservative replication**, as the new DNA contains one 'old' polynucleotide (the template) and one 'new' polynucleotide. Base-pairing is important because exposed bases on the template DNA determine which nucleotide is next in the sequence. Cytosine always pairs with guanine and adenine always pairs with thymine. Replication happens during interphase of the cell cycle (see page 53).

Key facts you must know

Think of replication as a series of events with a beginning, a middle and an end.
- DNA unwinds.
- Hydrogen bonds holding the bases together are broken.
- Polynucleotide chains separate.
- Bases are exposed along both polynucleotide chains.
- Each chain acts as a template so a new chain can be built up, following the rules of base pairing — A–T and C–G.
- Free nucleotide molecules in the nucleus are put in position alongside the exposed bases — each nucleotide consists of sugar, base and three phosphates.
- As the nucleotides 'line up', they form a growing chain.
- Two of the phosphates from each nucleotide break off in a reaction that forms a covalent bond between the new nucleotide and the growing chain.
- DNA polymerase (an enzyme) joins the nucleotides in the correct sequence.
- Hydrogen bonds form between the bases on opposite polynucleotide chains — the template chain and the newly synthesised chain.
- DNA winds up again into a double helix. Replication is complete.

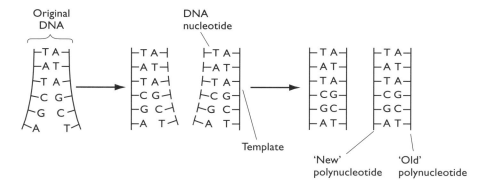

Figure 38 The stages of DNA replication shown in a very simple fashion

The evidence for this came from investigating replication in bacteria. Bacteria were grown on a special medium that made them make 'heavier' DNA. This was because the medium contained a heavy isotope of nitrogen. When the DNA was extracted and spun in a centrifuge it formed a layer towards the bottom of the tube — lower than normal DNA with the lighter isotope of nitrogen. When the bacteria were removed from this medium and grown in a normal medium, they made DNA which was inter-mediate between the other two forms of DNA. This showed that part of the DNA was 'old' and part was made of newly synthesised DNA (see Figure 39). Look carefully at the way the DNA has been drawn at the bottom of the diagram.

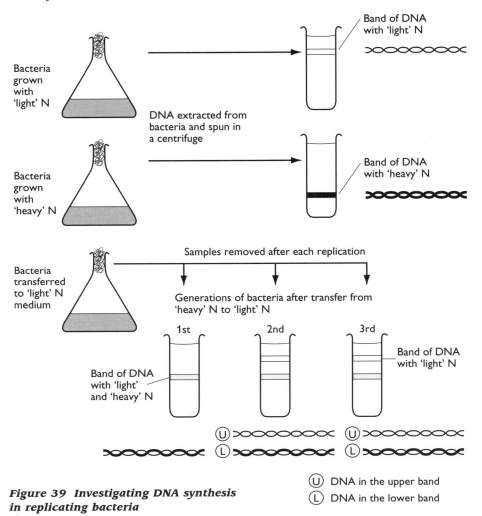

Figure 39 Investigating DNA synthesis in replicating bacteria

Ⓤ DNA in the upper band
Ⓛ DNA in the lower band

One gene, one polypeptide

Key concepts you must understand

Genes are made of DNA. They are lengths of nucleotides with a specific sequence of bases. A gene determines the sequence of amino acids in a polypeptide, coding for the order in which amino acids are put together. In DNA there are four bases (A, T, C and G). There are 20 different types of amino acid (e.g. glycine, alanine and cysteine).

So four bases have to code for 20 amino acids. The chart below shows how this could be done.

Number of bases in a code	Number of amino acids that could be coded	Outcome
1 (i.e. A, T, C and G)	4	Not enough
2 (e.g. AA, TT, AC, GA)	16	Not enough
3 (e.g. AAA, TAT, CAG)	64	More than enough

The simplest code that will work is a triplet code (using three bases). However, this gives 64 different codes when only 20 are required. This means that there are several codes for each amino acid. For example, the DNA triplet codes for glycine are CCA, CCC, CCG, CCT.

As well as the codes for the amino acids, there are three 'stop' codes which indicate the end of a sequence (e.g. ACT). The triplet code for the different amino acids is called the **genetic code** (see Question 5 on page 75 for the full version).

Protein synthesis

Key concepts you must understand

Protein synthesis means making proteins by assembling amino acids using information stored in DNA. This relies on the precision of base-pairing, so that the sequence of bases in DNA is transferred, via RNA, to the ribosomes.

Key facts you must know

Protein synthesis happens in three stages:
- transcription
- amino acid activation
- translation

Transcription

Islet cells in the pancreas make protein insulin. It is only in these cells that the gene is switched on. The gene is a sequence of bases in DNA that instructs the cell how to assemble amino acids to make insulin. Every islet cell has two copies of this gene, but many copies are needed to send to the thousands of ribosomes in the cell to make the quantities of insulin required. Short-lived copies of the gene are made in transcription. The copies are molecules of messenger RNA (mRNA).
- The hydrogen bonds between the bases in the two polynucleotide chains separate in the area of DNA corresponding to the insulin gene.
- One chain (the coding polynucleotide chain) acts as a template for mRNA synthesis.

- Free RNA nucleotides in the nucleus pair up with the exposed bases on the template or coding chain.
- The nucleotides are joined together to form a polynucleotide — mRNA.
- mRNA leaves the nucleus through a nuclear pore.

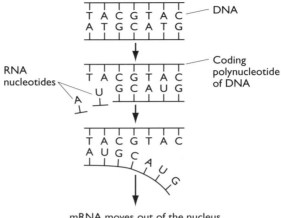

Figure 40 Transcription of the coding polynucleotide in DNA

Amino acid activation

In the cytoplasm, there are 61 different types of tRNA and 20 different amino acid molecules. The amino acids are 'identified' or 'tagged' by combining with tRNA molecules so that they have nucleotide 'labels'. The label is the anticodon. Enzymes in the cytoplasm attach amino acids to specific tRNA molecules. This is not a random process — each type of amino acid is identified by its own specific tRNA molecule.

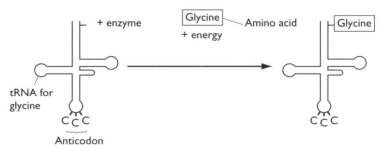

Figure 41 The enzyme shown here will only accept glycine and its specific tRNA molecule

Translation

- The mRNA molecule joins with a ribosome in the cytoplasm.
- Each ribosome has two sites to hold two tRNA molecules at the same time. Each tRNA molecule is attached to an amino acid.

- Each tRNA molecule has a sequence of three bases (anticodon) that pairs with three bases (codon) on mRNA.
- tRNA and mRNA pair together, following the rules of base pairing.
- A condensation reaction occurs between the amino acids to form a peptide bond.
- The ribosome moves along the mRNA molecule, 'reading' the sequence of bases.
- As this happens, a polypeptide grows by the addition of new amino acid molecules.
- When an amino acid has joined to the growing chain, its tRNA molecule leaves the ribosome to attach to another amino acid.
- When the ribosome reaches the stop codon, the polypeptide breaks away.
- The cell processes the polypeptide, perhaps by combining it with other polypeptides to form a protein with quaternary structure. This happens in the cells that make haemoglobin (see page 25 for a description of the structure of haemoglobin).

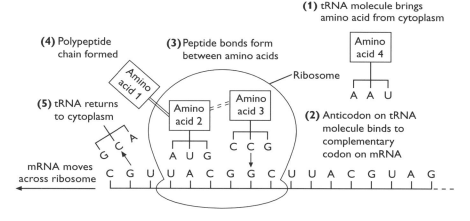

Figure 42 Translation

DNA, proteins and enzymes

Key concepts you must understand

Enzymes are produced inside cells by protein synthesis. Some enzymes, for example lipase (see page 22), are made of a single polypeptide. The gene for lipase is a sequence of nucleotides that codes for the amino acids that make this enzyme. Cells in the pancreas (not the islet cells) make lipase. When they do this, the genes are activated so that mRNA is produced. mRNA then travels to the ribosomes, which use it as the code to assemble amino acids in the correct sequence.

Links Decoding the human genome has involved 'reading' sequences of bases throughout DNA. The implications for this are considered in Module 2802.

Genetic manipulation

Key concepts you must understand

All DNA has the same structure. This means that pieces of DNA from one organism can be incorporated into the DNA of another. Cells that contain 'foreign' DNA (i.e. DNA from another organism) will still translate the code and make the same polypeptide. This is the basis of genetic manipulation, or genetic engineering. This sounds simple, but there are problems with taking genes from one organism and inserting them into another. Often, when animal and plant genes are inserted into bacteria, the correct sequence of amino acids is produced, but bacteria cannot fold and cut the polypeptide to produce a functional protein.

Key facts you must know

Bacteria are used in genetic engineering to produce multiple copies of genes.

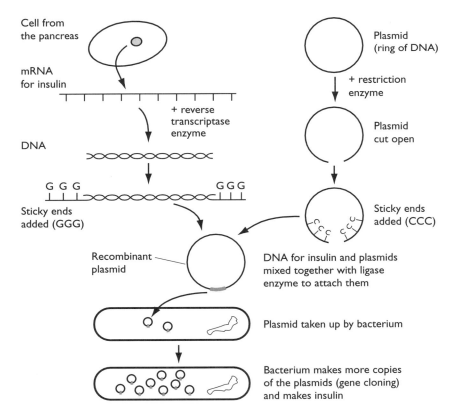

Figure 43 Gene cloning — using bacteria to make multiple copies of human genes

Human genes that have been copied in this way are those for insulin and factor VIII.

Human insulin

Diabetics do not have sufficient insulin to control the concentration of glucose in their blood. In the past, insulin was collected from pig pancreas tissue. Now, bacteria and yeast cells are genetically modified to make insulin.

Human factor VIII

People who suffer from the inherited disease haemophilia lack a blood clotting protein, so it takes their blood a long time to clot. They lack a functioning gene to synthesise a protein called factor VIII. The gene is inserted into the DNA of cells derived from hamster ovaries. These are grown in culture and produce the protein. This is a much safer method of production than collecting it from donated blood, as that carries the risk of transferring blood-borne viruses such as hepatitis B and HIV.

Nuclear division

The role of mitosis

Key concepts you must understand

Multicellular organisms, such as animals and plants, grow in two basic ways: either the cells increase in size or they divide by mitosis. Cells increase in size by making new molecules, such as phospholipids and proteins, new membranes and new organelles. Cells cannot grow like this indefinitely. When they reach a certain size, diffusion distances between the cell membrane and the centre of the cell become too great and not enough oxygen reaches the mitochondria for respiration. Also, there is not a large enough surface for diffusion of oxygen and carbon dioxide to occur relative to the size of the cell.

Key facts you must know

Animals repair themselves following wounding or natural processes such as giving birth. Plants also repair themselves after wounding, for example when they are damaged by storms. New cells are produced in much the same way as during growth.

Some animals and plants reproduce asexually, by budding or growing parts that separate from the parent. Asexual reproduction is really just a form of growth, so it also involves mitosis.

All the cells produced in growth and repair have the same genetic information as the parent cell; all the cells have the same DNA and the same genes. Therefore, all the cells can function together as one unit. This is also an advantage in asexual reproduction. New individuals are all genetically the same as the parent and are likely to survive in the same environment as the parent. This is especially the case with plants that spread by asexual reproduction, such as bluebells growing in a wood.

Cancer

Key concepts you must understand

Growth and division of cells by mitosis is carefully controlled in organisms by certain genes. Sometimes these genes change, so that control is lost and cells start to grow uncontrollably to form lumps or tumours which stay in one place or spread through the body. These cancerous growths occur in both animals and plants. Tumours can be benign (usually harmless) or malignant. Malignant tumours are described as cancers because they are invasive and spread throughout the body, pressing on blood vessels and blocking passageways. If untreated, they are likely to be fatal.

Key facts you must know

Cancers start because genes mutate. Mutations occur in DNA all the time; often these are small changes to the base sequence, so they have the potential to change the structure and function of proteins and be harmful. But there are special mechanisms in cells to repair changes in DNA, so these mutations have no effect. However, not all mutations are repaired and some can be very serious.

As we age, mutations accumulate. Some mutations affect the genes that control cell division, causing the changes outlined above. These mutations are caused by environmental factors known as mutagens. When mutagens cause cells to become cancerous they are called carcinogens.

Some factors and the resulting human cancers are listed in the table below.

Factor	Human cancer
Ultraviolet light	Skin
Tar in tobacco smoke	Lung
Asbestos	Lung
Viruses	Burkitt's lymphoma (a cancer of the lymphatic system)
Genes	Retinoblastoma (a cancer of the eye)

Links Lung cancer is a topic in Module 2802. When you study it, recall how lung cancer is caused.

Mitosis

Key concepts you must understand

Chromosomes are made of DNA and protein. DNA is the important molecule as it codes for all the features of an organism. The proteins in chromosomes help with DNA packing. DNA is a long molecule, wound around proteins to make chromosomes.

When you look at a dividing cell through a microscope, you can see chromosomes if they have been stained. Sometimes it is possible to see separate chromosomes, especially at metaphase during mitosis.

Key facts you must know

During interphase of the cell cycle, DNA replication occurs, so that each chromosome has two identical DNA molecules. These are wound around proteins to form chromatids — joined together at the centromere. Now there are two copies of each molecule of DNA within one chromosome. During anaphase of mitosis, these separate and move apart to opposite ends of the cell. At telophase, there are two nuclei with identical genetic information and the same number of chromosomes as the original cell. The key stages of mitosis are outlined in Figure 44.

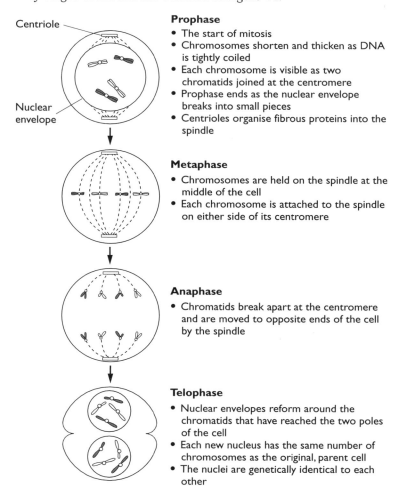

Prophase
- The start of mitosis
- Chromosomes shorten and thicken as DNA is tightly coiled
- Each chromosome is visible as two chromatids joined at the centromere
- Prophase ends as the nuclear envelope breaks into small pieces
- Centrioles organise fibrous proteins into the spindle

Metaphase
- Chromosomes are held on the spindle at the middle of the cell
- Each chromosome is attached to the spindle on either side of its centromere

Anaphase
- Chromatids break apart at the centromere and are moved to opposite ends of the cell by the spindle

Telophase
- Nuclear envelopes reform around the chromatids that have reached the two poles of the cell
- Each new nucleus has the same number of chromosomes as the original, parent cell
- The nuclei are genetically identical to each other

Figure 44 Stages in mitosis

Links Replication must occur before mitosis. Each chromosome must have two DNA molecules so that they can be divided between the two new cells. The details of replication are on pages 44 and 45. The best way to understand the events that occur in mitosis is to watch a time-lapse film of a cell dividing. You can find some animations of mitosis at: www.biology.arizona.edu/cell_bio/tutorials/cell_cycle/main.html. If you are taking the practical examination, you should study the stages of mitosis in a root tip preparation.

Chromosomes and life cycles

Key concepts you must understand

Diploid cells have two sets of chromosomes. This means there are two chromosomes of each type. In humans, the diploid number is 46; there are 23 pairs of chromosomes. We inherit our chromosomes from our parents. One set of chromosomes is inherited from our father, one from our mother. So one chromosome of each type is paternal and the other is maternal in origin. Think about the sex chromosomes, X and Y, in boys. Males have one X and one Y. A boy inherits his X chromosome from his mother and his Y chromosome from his father. In the same way, he inherits one of each pair of chromosomes from his father and the other from his mother.

Key facts you must know

Homologous chromosomes have the same
- shape and size
- position of the centromere
- genes

It is possible to see homologous pairs of chromosomes under the microscope. Computers can scan photographs of cells taken at metaphase of mitosis. They look for similarities, particularly in the banding patterns that chromosomes have when treated with certain dyes. The images of the chromosomes are then put into pairs.

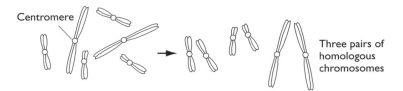

Centromere

Three pairs of homologous chromosomes

Figure 45 Homologous chromosomes

During sexual reproduction, gametes (sex cells) fuse at fertilisation. From generation to generation, the diploid number remains constant. There is no doubling of the chromosome number with each generation, as this would lead to cells with huge numbers of chromosomes and very large quantities of DNA. The diploid number stays constant from generation to generation because the number of chromosomes in gametes is half the diploid number. Meiosis halves the chromosome number. It is sometimes called reduction division because of this.

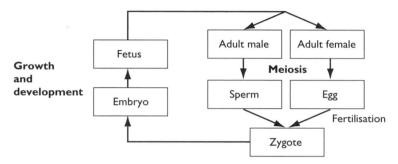

Figure 46 The position of meiosis in the human life cycle

Links There is much more about meiosis at A2. For now, remember that it halves the chromosome number and occurs in life cycles with sexual reproduction.

Energy and ecosystems

Ecological terminology

Key facts you must know

The key ecological terms are defined in the table below.

Term	Definition	Examples
Habitat	A place where an individual, population or community lives	Rock pool, pond, stream, meadow, forest
Niche	The role of an organism in a community — where it is, what it does, how it feeds, how it behaves	A crab that hides in a rock pool, scavenging on dead animal matter
Population	A group of individuals of the same species in the same area at the same time; males and females within the population can breed with each other	All the crabs of one species on a rocky shore
Community	All populations of plants, animals and microorganisms in a well-defined area at the same time	All the organisms on a rocky shore
Ecosystem	A community and the abiotic factors that influence it; interactions between organisms within the community	A rocky shore community and physical features, such as wave action, temperature etc.

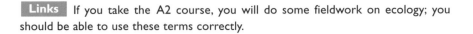 **Links** If you take the A2 course, you will do some fieldwork on ecology; you should be able to use these terms correctly.

Energy flow in ecosystems

Key concepts you must understand

Energy is an important concept in biology. In ecology, you need to think of energy being transferred through food chains and food webs. In most ecosystems, light energy is captured by green plants to drive photosynthesis. The energy is used to convert the simple inorganic compounds carbon dioxide and water into complex organic molecules, such as sugars and amino acids. This provides biological molecules for the growth of plants and food for animals that feed on those plants. There are some ecosystems where there is no light, for example in caves. Animals that live in caves often survive on the dead bodies of organisms that fall into or get washed into the cave.

Key facts you must know

- **Trophic levels** are feeding levels in a food chain. Examples are producers and consumers.
- **Producers** are organisms that trap sunlight and make use of the energy in photo-synthesis. They have pigments, such as chlorophyll, to absorb light energy. They start many food chains. On land, green plants are the main producers. In the sea, photosynthetic algae, such as seaweeds and microscopic phytoplankton, are the main producers.
- **Consumers** are organisms that cannot carry out photosynthesis and must take in their energy in the form of complex organic compounds.
- **Food chains** show a simple relationship between producers and consumers in an ecosystem. Here is a marine example:

  phytoplankton ⟶ zooplankton ⟶ small herbivorous ⟶ large carnivorous
                                                   fish   fish
- **Food webs** are much more complex. They show all the feeding relationships within a community. Figure 47 shows a simplified example.

Energy flow in food webs and food chains is shown by the direction of the arrows. Energy flows from producer to primary consumer to secondary consumer to tertiary consumer, and so on. Energy is not recycled. Instead, it leaves the ecosystem as 'low-grade heat energy' which warms the atmosphere.

Food chains tend to be short. This is because much of the energy that enters the organisms at one trophic level is used by those organisms and is not available to be consumed by the next trophic level. Energy is lost from the organisms because of:
- respiration
- heat loss

This means that only a small percentage of the energy that enters a trophic level becomes stored in the bodies of the organisms in that trophic level to be eaten by those of the next.

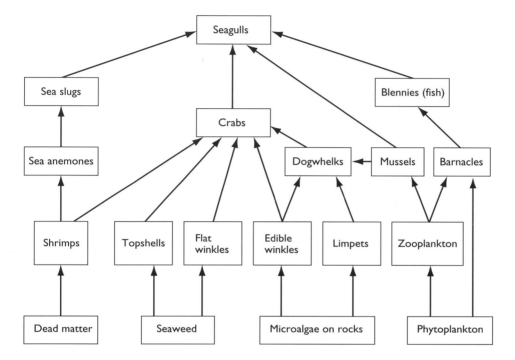

Figure 47 A food web for a rocky shore community

Plants to primary consumers

Little of the light energy striking plants is used in photosynthesis because:

- some light is reflected from the surfaces of leaves
- some light passes straight through leaves
- chloroplast enzymes do not function efficiently if it is too cold
- carbon dioxide is sometimes in short supply

At best, our crop plants may pass on to us 5% of the energy that strikes their leaves. In natural ecosystems, the percentage is even lower than this. Not all of the energy in plants reaches the primary consumers, as some plant matter is not eaten. Much will die and decay before it is eaten by consumers that graze on plants, while some of the material that is eaten cannot be digested. Dead plant material will be eaten by detritivores, such as earthworms, or pass to the decomposers (fungi and bacteria).

Primary consumers to secondary consumers

Secondary consumers, such as antelope, feed on plants. Their energy input is equivalent to the energy content of all the grass and other plants that they eat. Some are preyed on by predators. The energy in the antelope that is eaten by predators is the energy transferred to the next trophic level. About 10% of the energy entering the primary consumer trophic level is passed to the secondary trophic level. In this example:

- the antelope uses energy in keeping warm (especially at night)
- it moves about in search of food
- it uses energy in reproduction
- not all the antelope's body is eaten
- not all of the antelope eaten by the predator is digested and absorbed

The only energy transferred to the next trophic level is energy in the flesh of the animal. As a percentage of the energy input from the producers, that is very small.

Links If organisms are to survive, they must gain sufficient energy. Competition for energy resources is an important aspect of survival, and organisms are adapted for this. Plants have strategies for absorbing sufficient light; consumers have ways of obtaining sufficient food and not losing it to competitors. These ideas are the basis for understanding adaptation, competition and selection at A2.

Cycling nitrogen

Key concepts you must understand

Nitrogen is important because it is part of many biological molecules, such as:
- amino acids and proteins
- nucleotides and nucleic acids

Key facts you must know

There is a huge quantity of nitrogen in the atmosphere. About 80% of the air is nitrogen in the form of the gas dinitrogen (N_2), in which there is a strong triple bond between the nitrogen atoms ($N \equiv N$). Some organisms can utilise dinitrogen by using energy to break the triple bond and combining nitrogen atoms with hydrogen to form ammonium ions. This is called nitrogen fixation. This is how some bacteria, such as *Rhizobium*, get their nitrogen. *Rhizobium* lives inside swellings (nodules) on the roots of legumes, such as peas and beans. It is provided with energy in the form of sugars by the legume and in return supplies fixed nitrogen to the plant.

Most organisms take in nitrogen that is already 'fixed' — it is combined with another element such as hydrogen or oxygen. Plants absorb simple forms of fixed nitrogen, such as ammonium or nitrate ions. Animals obtain nitrogen by eating food containing complex nitrogenous compounds, such as proteins.

There is only a limited supply of 'fixed' nitrogen in ecosystems and the supply of nitrate ions (and to a lesser extent ammonium ions) depends on the action of microorganisms that make use of nitrogen compounds and recycle them.

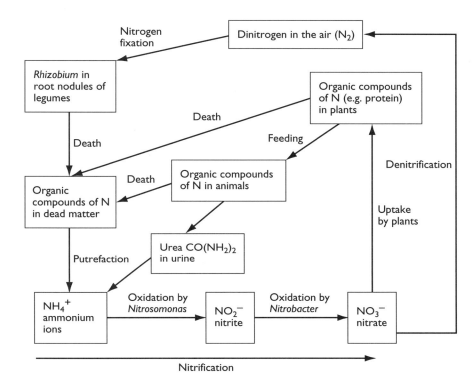

Figure 48 Part of the nitrogen cycle (note the importance of bacteria in recycling nitrogen compounds)

Use Figure 48 to find the following processes:

Plants
- absorb nitrate ions (NO_3^-) from the soil
- convert nitrate ions to ammonium ions (NH_4^+) and use them to make amino acids
- convert amino acids into proteins

Herbivores
- eat plants and digest proteins into amino acids
- use amino acids to make their own proteins (e.g. haemoglobin and collagen)
- break down excess proteins and amino acids to form ammonium ions
- convert ammonium ions to urea
- excrete nitrogenous waste (e.g. ammonium ions and urea)
- produce dung which contains proteins
- die to leave dead bodies containing proteins

Putrefying bacteria
- digest proteins in dead organisms into amino acids
- convert amino acids into ammonium ions

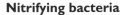

Nitrifying bacteria

- convert ammonium ions into nitrite ions (*Nitrosomonas*)
- convert nitrite ions into nitrate ions (*Nitrobacter*)

Nitrification, carried out by nitrifying bacteria, is how they gain their source of energy. *Nitrosomonas* oxidises ammonium into nitrite with the release of energy, which is used to convert carbon dioxide into organic molecules. It is a process similar to photosynthesis but, instead of using light energy, uses energy released from chemical reactions. The process is called chemosynthesis.

The nitrate released by *Nitrobacter* is available for plants to absorb.

Links Nothing works better than the nitrogen cycle to bring together different aspects of biology. If you look through the section above, you will find trophic levels, food chains, different ways of feeding, biological molecules (amino acids and proteins) and nutrition of bacteria, such as *Nitrobacter* and *Rhizobium*. You could also think about the chemical industry manufacturing nitrogen fertilisers and their use in agriculture. Human sewage contains ammonium ions and urea. Sewage works make use of the changes in the nitrogen cycle to convert these harmful compounds to nitrate ions and dinitrogen. This saves rivers and streams from becoming polluted. You might study aspects of the cycling of nitrogen in the A2 course.

Questions
&
Answers

This section is not exactly like the unit test. Each question represents one of the sections of the module. The total mark for the questions is 91, whereas the total in the unit test will be 60 marks.

As you read through this section, you will discover that Candidate A gains full marks for all the questions. This is so you can see what high-grade answers look like. Remember that the minimum for grade A is about 80% of the maximum mark (in this case around 72 marks). Candidate B makes a lot of mistakes — often these are ones that examiners encounter frequently. I will tell you how many marks Candidate B gets for each question. If the overall mark for the paper is about 40% of the total (around 36 marks), then the candidate will have passed at grade E standard. Use these benchmarks when trying the questions yourself.

Examiner's comments

Candidates' answers are followed by examiner's comments. These are preceded by the icon [e] and indicate where credit is due. In the weaker answers they also point out areas for improvement, specific problems and common errors, such as lack of clarity, weak or non-existent development, irrelevance, misinterpretation of the question and mistaken meanings of terms.

Cells, tissues and organs

Figure 1 is a drawing made from an electron micrograph of an epithelial cell.

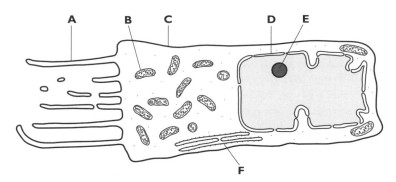

Figure 1

(a) With reference to Figure 1, name:
    (i) the type of epithelial cell shown   (1 mark)
    (ii) the structures labelled A to F   (6 marks)

(b) Use the most appropriate word or words to complete the paragraph below on cells and tissues in a leaf.

The tissues in a leaf form a sort of sandwich. Between the upper and lower
.... are the palisade and spongy .... cells which are
rich in chloroplasts. Veins in the leaf are composed of vascular tissue. Xylem is
a tissue made of several cell types. The main water conducting cells known as
.... form hollow tubes and have no end walls. Sieve tubes in
the phloem are composed of sieve tube elements and .... cells.
The transport of .... occurs in the phloem.   (5 marks)

                                                   Total: 12 marks

■ ■ ■

Candidates' answers to Question 1

Candidate A
(a) (i) Ciliated epithelial cell

Candidate B
(a) (i) Squamous epithelium

    e Candidate A has identified the cell correctly. Candidate B has given the name of a
    tissue and not a cell *and* has chosen the wrong one! A squamous cell would be thin
    and would not be ciliated like this one. Always look carefully at the information you
    are given to see if there are any clues.

question

Candidate A

(a) (ii) A — cilium; B — mitochondrion; C — cell membrane; D — nuclear membrane; E — nucleolus; F — rough endoplasmic reticulum

Candidate B

(a) (ii) A — cilia; B — mitochondria; C — cell wall; D — nuclear; E — nucleous; F — endoplasmic reticulum

> Candidate A has given six correct answers; Candidate B gains marks for A and B even though the answers given are the plurals. This is an animal cell, not a plant cell, so C cannot be the cell wall. Many candidates write about 'cell walls' in animals, often when they are referring to a 'wall of cells'. If you are writing about a layer of cells lining a tube in the body (e.g. trachea, oviduct, oesophagus), then you should refer to an epithelium. The trachea and oviduct are lined by ciliated epithelia; the oesophagus is lined by a squamous epithelium. For D, Candidate B has written 'nuclear' but not finished the answer (0 marks) and, for E, has written 'nucleous' instead of **nucleolus**. No mark is awarded for this because the word sounds like 'nucleus' rather than nucleolus. For F, endoplasmic reticulum is correct, although Candidate A has given a more precise answer. Candidate B gains 3 marks for part (a).

Candidate A

(b) Epidermis; mesophyll; vessel elements; companion; sugars

Candidate B

(b) Epidermis; mesophyll; vessels; companion; starch

> Candidate A has all the answers correct, although it would be more precise to write 'sucrose' rather than 'sugars', since glucose is not transported in the phloem. Candidate B gets 3 marks. A xylem vessel refers to many xylem vessel elements joined together in a long tube, so 'vessels' is not correct in the context of the passage. Starch is insoluble and is not transported through the phloem. It is quite difficult to remember the difference between xylem (the tissue), xylem vessels (columns of hollow cells joined together) and vessel elements (the individual cells). The same thing applies to phloem (the tissue), sieve tubes (columns of cells) and sieve tube elements (the cells that form the sieve tubes). It is worth making some drawings to remind yourself of the differences.

> **Candidate B gets 6 marks out of 12 for this question.**

Biological molecules

Some proteins are composed of a single polypeptide.

(a) Explain the meaning of the term *primary structure of a protein*. (1 mark)

Figure 1 is a ribbon diagram that shows the secondary structure and the tertiary structure of a globular protein.

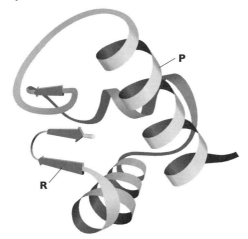

Figure 1

(b) Name the parts of the protein labelled P and R. (2 marks)

(c) List *three* bonds that stabilise the tertiary structure of proteins. (3 marks)

(d) Explain how the tertiary structure of a globular protein is important in determining its function. (2 marks)

(e) Explain why the protein shown in Figure 1 does not show quaternary structure. (1 mark)

Collagen and DNA are biological molecules that both have a helical structure.

(f) Describe *two* ways in which the structure of DNA differs from that of collagen. (2 marks)

(g) Explain how the helical structure of collagen helps to make it a very strong molecule. (1 mark)

Total: 12 marks

■ ■ ■

Candidates' answers to Question 2

Candidate A
(a) Amino acid sequence

Candidate B
(a) The order in which the amino acids are put together

> *e* Both candidates gain the mark here. Candidate A has answered more efficiently through knowing a concise definition of the term.

question

Candidate A

(b) P — alpha-helix; R — beta-pleated sheet

Candidate B

(b) P — helix; R — beta sheet

> *e* Once again, both these answers are rewarded, but Candidate A is far more accurate.

Candidate A

(c) Hydrogen; disulphide; ionic

Candidate B

(c) Hydrogen; ionic; disulphide; hydrophobic

> *e* All these answers are correct. However, Candidate B is showing off! The question asks for three bonds, not four. If any of the first three had been wrong (for example peptide), the examiner would have awarded only 2 marks.

Candidate A

(d) This makes a 3D shape. In enzymes, the shape of the active site means that only one type of substrate fits in.

Candidate B

(d) Tertiary structure is to do with the folding of the protein.

> *e* Candidate A has given a good answer to a difficult question by using knowledge of enzymes and active sites. 2 marks are awarded here — for the ideas of 3D shape and the substrate 'fitting' into the protein. Candidate B gains no marks, as there is no attempt to link structure with function; folding could also refer to secondary structure.

Candidate A

(e) There is only one polypeptide.

Candidate B

(e) It is not made up of four polypeptides.

> *e* It is a common mistake to think that quaternary structure means that there are four polypeptides making up a protein, so Candidate B is wrong here. There are two reasons for this: quaternary refers to the *fourth level* of organisation and haemoglobin (which is the only globular protein named in the specification) has four polypeptides. Candidate A is correct and gains a mark, although it would be an idea to add that proteins with quaternary structure have two or more polypeptides.

Candidate A

(f) DNA is a double helix, collagen is a triple helix; DNA is made of nucleotides, collagen is made of amino acids.

Candidate B

(f) Collagen is made of three polypeptides; DNA is a double helix.

e Candidate A gains both marks here because both molecules (DNA and collagen) are mentioned, so the difference is clear. Candidate B does not give a complete comparison between the molecules. The question asks for ways in which the structure of DNA differs from collagen and therefore the examiner is looking for two facts about DNA. It is not clear from the statement 'Collagen is made of three polypeptides' that DNA is not made of polypeptides. 'DNA is a double helix' is a way in which DNA differs from collagen, and so gains the candidate 1 mark.

Candidate A

(g) There are many hydrogen bonds between the three polypeptides, which fit very closely together.

Candidate B

(g) The polypeptides fit closely together, making a strong molecule.

e Candidate A's answer includes the hydrogen bonding between the polypeptides, but this is not mentioned by Candidate B. It is not sufficient to say that the molecule is strong simply because the polypeptides fit closely together.

e **Candidate B is awarded 7 marks out of 12 for this question.**

Enzymes

There are several different models that are used to explain how enzymes function. Two of them are 'lock-and-key' and 'induced-fit'.

(a) Show, by means of clear diagrams, how one of these models is used to explain how enzymes function. Write notes about the diagrams you draw to help your explanation. (5 marks)

A student investigated the effect of temperature on the rate of a reaction catalysed by a protease (protein-digesting) enzyme. The student chose the following temperatures: 5, 15, 25, 35, 45, 55 and 65°C, and took one result at each temperature. The results are shown in Figure 1.

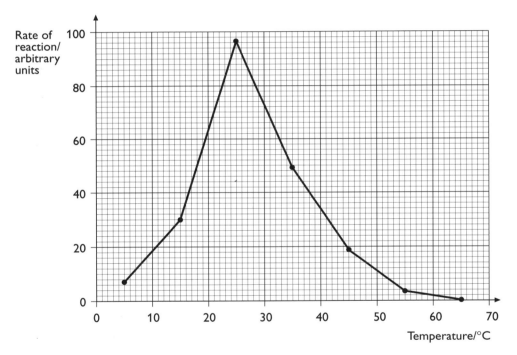

Figure 1

(b) Describe and explain the results of this investigation. Use the information in Figure 1 to help your answer.

In this question, 1 mark is awarded for the quality of written communication. (7 marks)

(c) Suggest *three* ways in which the student could improve this investigation. (3 marks)

Total: 15 marks

Candidates' answers to Question 3

Candidate A

(a)

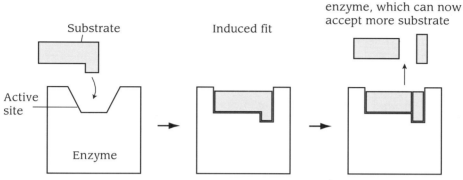

Product molecules leave enzyme, which can now accept more substrate

Active site 'moulds' around the substrate — this is induced fit

The substrate fits into active site to form enzyme–substrate complex

When the substrate is in the active site, there is a good fit, because the substrate has a shape that is complementary to the active site (it has the opposite shape)

Substrate breaks into two products — this is now an enzyme–product complex

Candidate B

(a)

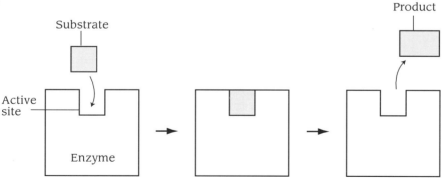

✏ Candidate A has given a very full answer, with plenty of explanatory notes around the diagrams of the induced fit model. Candidate B has only labelled the diagrams and has not explained that the substrate molecule is a complementary shape to the active site and fits into it. This is the essential point about the lock-and-key model. The question asks how the models are used to explain how enzymes function, so it is important to link the model to the mode of action of enzymes (described on page 28). Candidate B gets 2 marks here for showing how the enzyme and substrate fit together and for identifying the active site.

Candidate A

(b) The highest rate of reaction was at 25°C (96.5 units). This may be the optimum temperature, but it is impossible to be sure as it could be anywhere between 15 and 35°C. There are no results for other temperatures in this range. The rate was lower at the temperatures used above and below 25°C. There was no enzyme activity at 65°C.

Enzymes do not work well at low temperatures. This is because reactions only occur when enzyme molecules collide with substrate molecules to form enzyme–substrate complexes. At low temperatures, there is little kinetic energy. As the temperature increases, there is more kinetic energy and collisions occur more frequently. At high temperatures (e.g. 65°C) enzymes are denatured and so do not work. This is because the bonds that hold enzymes' molecules together (hydrogen, ionic) break as the enzyme molecule vibrates. This destroys the active site which is then not the right shape to take the substrate molecules.

Candidate B

(b) Enzymes work faster at high temperatures. The graph shows that the best reaction happens at 25°C. This is the optimum temperature. Molecules move about and collide. This happens much more often at the optimum temperature than at other temperatures. This means that substrate molecules get broken down much faster. Nothing happens at 65°C because the enzyme is denatured. The substrate's active site will not fit into the enzyme and so no reaction takes place.

The question asks the candidates to *describe* and *explain*. Candidate A has planned the answer so that the first section is a description of the graph. The candidate is right to say that we do not know the optimum temperature. The question is based around real data that a student could have collected in a practical class. There is uncertainty about where to place a line of best fit, so the points have been joined with straight lines. Candidate A has described this very well and has also quoted data from the graph. The candidate has then *explained* the results in terms of collisions and used appropriate terminology, such as *active site* and *enzyme–substrate complex*. Denaturation has been explained fully. Candidate B has not really *described* the information shown in the graph and the last sentence contains a common error about active sites. The active site is part of the enzyme and *not* the substrate. Candidate B only gains 3 marks here.

Candidate A

(c) By using some lower temperatures; by using more intermediate temperatures; by carrying out more results at each temperature and calculating averages.

Candidate B

(c) By using a buffer solution to keep the pH constant; by repeating the experiment; by doing more temperatures.

e Candidate A has given three very clear suggestions based on the information in the question. Candidate B makes a very good suggestion about controlling another variable — pH. You should remember that pH is a variable that affects enzymes and that it can be kept constant using a buffer solution. In this case, the student could use a buffer solution that gives the optimum pH. 'Repeating the experiment' is not really a suitable answer on its own. Similarly, 'doing more temperatures' is not a precise answer. Candidate B gets 1 mark here.

e **Candidate B gains 6 marks out of 15 for this question.**

uestion

Cell membranes and transport

Figure 1 is a diagram of the cell surface of a red blood cell. The arrows labelled 1 to 4 show pathways taken by substances as they cross the membrane.

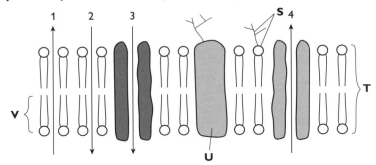

Figure 1

(a) Name the structures labelled **S** to **V**. (4 marks)

(b) Complete the table by placing a tick (✓) or a cross (✗) in the boxes to show which of the pathways could apply in each case.

Movement taking place	1	2	3	4
Facilitated diffusion				
Chloride ions diffuse into the cell				
Water leaves the cell by osmosis				
Oxygen diffuses into and out of the cell				

(4 marks)

(c) Some cells engulf small particles of food by endocytosis. Describe how this process occurs. (3 marks)

Some roots were divided into two batches, A and B. Both were kept in solutions containing potassium ions. The roots in batch A were kept in a solution without oxygen; the roots in batch B were supplied with oxygen. The quantity of potassium ions absorbed by the roots was measured over several hours. The results are shown in Figure 2.

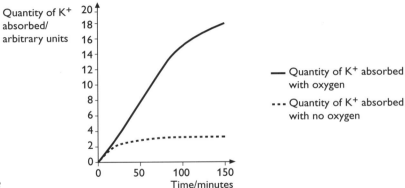

Figure 2

(d) Explain how the information in Figure 2 supports the hypothesis that potassium ions were absorbed by active transport in the roots. **(4 marks)**

Total: 15 marks

■ ■ ■

Candidates' answers to Question 4

Candidate A

(a) S — glycolipid; T — phospholipid bilayer; U — glycoprotein; V — phospholipid

Candidate B

(a) S — lipid; T — membrane; U — protein; V — phospholipid

> ℯ Candidate A has identified all the structures correctly. Candidate B has not noticed that S has a carbohydrate chain and is therefore a glycolipid — 'lipid' is not precise enough. The same applies to U, which also has a sugar chain on it. Candidate B has not realised that the bracket labelled T refers to the two layers of phospholipids. The question says that this is a diagram of a membrane! Candidate B gains 1 mark. The specification gives a list of structures in the membrane and you are expected to be able to identify them from diagrams like this one.

Candidate A

(b)

Movement taking place	1	2	3	4
Facilitated diffusion	✗	✗	✓	✓
Chloride ions diffuse into the cell	✗	✗	✓	✗
Water leaves the cell by osmosis	✓	✗	✗	✓
Oxygen diffuses into and out of the cell	✓	✓	✓	✓

Candidate B

(b)

Movement taking place	1	2	3	4
Facilitated diffusion	✗	✗	✓	✓
Chloride ions diffuse into the cell	✗	✓	✗	✗
Water leaves the cell by osmosis	✓	✓		
Oxygen diffuses into and out of the cell	✓	✓		

> ℯ Candidate A gains all 4 marks here. Facilitated diffusion occurs through protein channels (as here) or through protein carriers (see page 39). Chloride ions move into and out of cells, but because they carry a charge they cannot pass through the phospholipid bilayer. This means that they have to enter and leave by facilitated diffusion. The top of the diagram is the outside of the membrane. This is shown by the presence of the sugar molecules on the glycolipid and glycoprotein; Candidate B has not noticed this. Also Candidate B has used a 'crossed tick'. The examiners cannot award marks if the answer is unclear. If you change your mind about an

answer, strike out the tick or cross and start again. There are no ticks or crosses in some of the boxes. The examiner can award a mark for the top row, but cannot award marks for the other three. In this case, the examiner is looking for correct *rows*.

Candidate A

(c) The small particles stick to the surface membrane; the membrane folds inwards around the particles. The membrane fuses to form a vacuole which then pinches off from the surface and enters the cytoplasm.

Candidate B

(c) The membrane makes a food vacuole and surrounds the food — phagocytosis.

🖉 This question carries 3 marks. Candidate A has made four points and gets full marks. Candidate B has only described the first stage of endocytosis and gains 1 mark. There is no mark here for identifying this type of endocytosis as phagocytosis.

Candidate A

(d) When oxygen was present, more and more potassium ions were taken up. But when there was no oxygen, a small quantity of ions were taken up and then no more. Oxygen must be important for the uptake of ions. Many ions are absorbed by active transport, which needs energy. Oxygen is required for respiration in the roots, which provides the energy for active transport. When there is no oxygen, there can be no respiration and so no active transport — as shown in the graph.

Candidate B

(d) Roots take up ions by active transport. There are carrier proteins in the membranes of root hairs that pump ions into the cells from the soil water. There is a low concentration of ions in the soil and a high concentration in the root hair. This is why active transport happens and not diffusion.

🖉 This is quite a difficult question, targeted at the candidates expected to gain A and B grades. Be prepared for questions that ask you to explain whether data support a hypothesis or not. This is a skill you should acquire during your course. Candidate B has made the error of writing about active transport without answering the question and gains no marks. Candidate A has used the information in the graph and knowledge of active transport to give an excellent answer. Look at the graph again. The uptake of potassium ions at the beginning is much the same in both groups of roots. This uptake is by diffusion, not by active uptake. The quantity remains constant in the sample without oxygen because there is no active uptake, so no more ions are absorbed.

🖉 **Candidate B is awarded 3 marks out of 15 for this question.**

DNA and RNA

The table below shows the genetic code in the form of messenger RNA codons. The table shows the codons and their respective amino acids. For example, the codons **UGU** and **UGC** code for the amino acid cysteine, which is indicated by cys in the table. Study the table carefully and then answer the questions that follow.

First base in codon	Second base in codon				Third base in codon
	U	**C**	**A**	**G**	
U	phe	ser	tyr	cys	U
	phe	ser	tyr	cys	C
	leu	ser	–	–	A
	leu	ser	–	trp	G
C	leu	pro	his	arg	U
	leu	pro	his	arg	C
	leu	pro	gln	arg	A
	leu	pro	gln	arg	G
A	ile	thr	asn	ser	U
	ile	thr	asn	ser	C
	ile	thr	lys	arg	A
	met	thr	lys	arg	G
G	val	ala	asp	gly	U
	val	ala	asp	gly	C
	val	ala	glu	gly	A
	val	ala	glu	gly	G

(a) (i) List two codons that code for the amino acid glycine (gly).   (1 mark)

    (ii) State the number of codons that code for the amino acid serine (ser).   (1 mark)

(b) Codons UAA, UGA and UAG are known as stop codons. Explain why.   (2 marks)

(c) Complete the table below to show the amino acid coded by the base sequence given.   (2 marks)

AUG	GCU	AAA	CUU	CAC	GCU
met					

'd) Explain why the genetic code is called a degenerate code.   (1 mark)

question

Figure 1 shows a translation occurring at a ribosome.

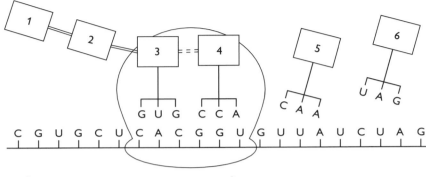

Figure 1

(e) **Describe the events that will occur as the ribosome shown in Figure 1 moves along the mRNA molecule to the end in the direction shown by the arrow. Credit will be given for the use of information from the table given at the beginning of the question in your answer.**

In this question, 1 mark is awarded for the quality of written communication.   (8 marks)

Total: 15 marks

■ ■ ■

Candidates' answers to Question 5

Candidate A

(a) (i) GGU, GGC

Candidate B

(a) (i) GGA, GGG

   e There are four possible answers. Both candidates are correct.

Candidate A

(a) (ii) 6

Candidate B

(a) (ii) 4

   e Candidate B has not found the two codons for serine that start with A — AGU and AGC. You should study tables like this carefully and systematically.

Candidate A

(b) They do not code for any of the amino acids. When a ribosome reaches a stop codon, translation comes to an end.

Candidate B

(b) Protein synthesis stops when it gets to one of these codons.

🖉 Candidate A makes two points and uses the information in the table. Candidate B has made the error of referring to 'it'. The examiner is not sure what the candidate means by 'it'. Protein synthesis is the whole process of transcription, amino acid activation and translation. This answer would have gained 1 mark if the candidate had written 'ribosome' instead of 'it'.

Candidate A

(c)

AUG	GCU	AAA	CUU	CAC	GCU
met	gly	lys	leu	his	ala

Candidate B

(c)

AUG	GCU	AAA	CUU	CAC	GCU
met	~~ala~~	lys	leu	his	ala

🖉 Candidate A's answer is correct and gains 2 marks. Candidate B's selection of amino acids is nearly correct, but one (ala) has been struck out and the correct amino acid (gly) has not been written in. This careless mistake costs 1 mark.

Candidate A

(d) There are more codons than necessary for each amino acid; for example, there are six for serine.

Candidate B

(d) For each amino acid there are three bases.

🖉 Candidate A has the right idea. The genetic code is described as degenerate as there are between two and six triplets for each amino acid. It is good to see the candidate using information from the table and a previous question as an example. This candidate has obviously followed the theme running through the question. Candidate B is confused and does not get a mark. The genetic code is a triplet code, but this is not what the examiner asked.

Candidate A

(e) In translation, ribosomes 'read' the messenger RNA (mRNA) in triplets. Each codon (e.g. AAA) codes for an amino acid. The amino acids are attached to specific transfer RNA molecules (tRNA) that have triplets of bases called anticodons. The anticodon for AAA is UUU as this follows the base pairing rule — A to U and C to G (U is found in RNA, whereas in DNA it is T).

In the diagram, there are two tRNA molecules sitting in the ribosome side by side. A peptide bond has formed between amino acids 3 and 4. Now the ribosome moves to the right and the tRNA molecule attached to amino acid 3 leaves the ribosome. There is an 'empty space' where the tRNA with amino acid 5 (which from the table is val) can fit. A peptide bond forms between 4 and 5 and the polypeptide grows longer. This continues with amino acid 6. I have drawn a picture of this below. Then there is a stop codon (UAG), so translation stops and the polypeptide leaves the ribosome.

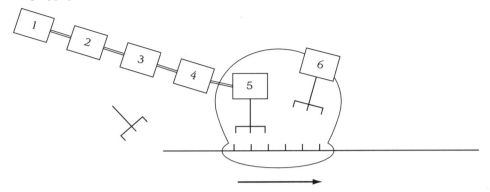

Candidate B

(e) Messenger RNA comes from the nucleus where it is produced by transcription. During transcription, DNA splits in half and one strand is copied as RNA. This leaves the nucleus and goes through pores in the nucleus to the RER. Here it joins to ribosomes and translation begins as you can see in the picture. When the ribosome moves to the right, the other two tRNA molecules with amino acids can fit in. They pair with the mRNA so the codon GUU pairs with CAA. This does not last long as then the tRNA leaves after the amino acid has joined with the poly-peptide. When the polypeptide leaves the ribosome, it goes to the Golgi body to be 'processed'. It may then be sent out of the cell in a vacuole.

    e Candidate A has made good use of the information in the table and has given a concise answer. The candidate obviously felt that including a diagram to show what happens next would make things clearer. This certainly helps the examiner award marks. However, do not draw diagrams for these extended answer questions unless they add something to your answer or, as here, help to make your meaning clearer. Candidate B has made several errors:

- the answer begins with transcription — this is not asked for
- little information from the table is used; for example, the amino acids are not identified
- the answer suggests that the ribosome moves along the mRNA two triplets at a time — this is not true
- the stop codon has not been used in the answer
- the answer ends with irrelevant information about what happens to the polypeptide *after* translation

    Candidate B gets 2 marks for referring to the base pairing and to tRNA leaving the ribosome. There is a QWC mark for this question. In this case, it is for writing an answer set out in a logical sequence, using appropriate technical terms. Candidate A gains the QWC mark, but Candidate B does not.

    e **Candidate B gains 4 marks out of 15 for this question.**

Nuclear division

Figure 1 is a diagram showing the life cycle of the Syrian hamster (diploid number = 44).

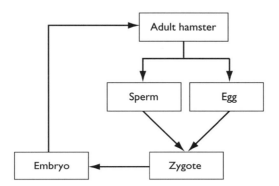

Figure 1

(a) Complete the table by writing in the number of chromosomes present at
each stage in the life cycle of the Syrian hamster. (5 marks)

Stage	Number of chromosomes
Adult	
Sperm	
Egg	
Zygote	
Embryo	

Figure 2 shows diagrams of five stages during the mitotic cell cycle of an animal, such as the Syrian hamster.

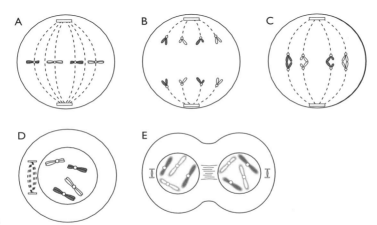

Figure 2

(b) Use the letters next to the diagrams in **Figure 2** to give the order in which the events occur during a mitotic cell cycle. The first is **D**. (2 marks)

(c) Explain why it is important that cells produced during growth are genetically identical to each other. (3 marks)

Total: 10 marks

■ ■ ■

Candidates' answers to Question 6

Candidate A

(a)

Stage	Number of chromosomes
Adult	44
Sperm	22
Egg	22
Zygote	44
Embryo	44

Candidate B

(a)

Stage	Number of chromosomes
Adult	46
Sperm	23
Egg	23
Zygote	46
Embryo	46

e Candidate B has made a common error which examiners see at GCSE and AS. The candidate has given the chromosome numbers for *human* cells, not for the animal asked in the question. This shows the importance of *reading the question*! This question would not seem out of place on a GCSE paper and you can expect to find some like this in AS unit tests. Candidate B has rushed at the question without reading and thinking.

Candidate A

(b) D, A, C, B, E

Candidate B

(b) D, A, B, C, E

e Candidate A has the correct sequence. Candidate B has made one mistake in the sequence by putting B before C, losing 1 out of 2 marks. However, if the candidate had written D, A, E, C, B, for example, no marks would be awarded, as there are two mistakes in this sequence. These questions are often tricky. Look carefully at the information given. The question says mitotic cell *cycle* and not just mitosis — interphase is included. Interphase is not a stage in mitosis, but is part of the cell cycle. DNA replication occurs during interphase and this must happen before a cell can divide by mitosis.

Candidate A

(c) This means the cells all have the same genes. This helps the body work together. For example, it means that all the cells in a tissue like ciliated epithelium will function together as a unit. Also, when there are any cells that have different genes (e.g. because they mutate), then the immune system gets rid of them. Cancer cells are like this and most of them are destroyed.

Candidate B

(c) All the cells are genetically identical because of mitosis and replication. The DNA is copied exactly during replication and then shared out between the two cells made in mitosis. This is why they are genetically identical.

e Candidate A has made a brave attempt at a difficult question, and manages full marks. When examiners ask about the significance or importance of something, they are asking a searching question. Candidate A has used knowledge to bring in the point about cancer cells. Candidate B has not answered the question. The answer explains 'how', but not 'why' — the last sentence is just a rewrite of the question.

e **Candidate B is awarded just 1 mark out of 10 for this question.**

Question 7

Energy flow

Some ecologists studied the energy flow through a community in a freshwater stream over a period of a year. They presented their results in the form of a diagram, which is shown in Figure 1. The numbers given are kilojoules per square metre per year ($kJ\,m^{-2}yr^{-1}$). The energy flow diagram shows, for example, that the plants in the ecosystem trapped 87 403 kJ m^{-2} of energy per year, but most of this (50 303 kJ) was lost as heat in respiration.

Figure 1

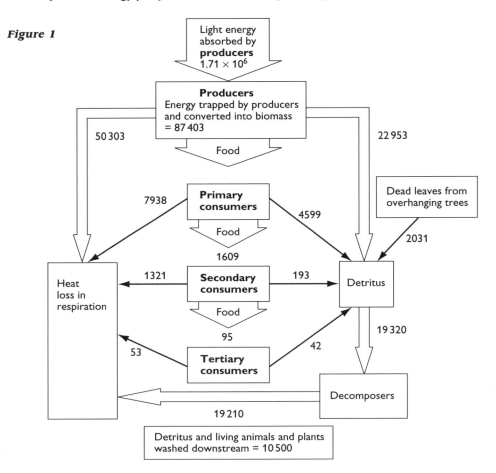

Study the energy flow diagram carefully before answering the questions.

(a) State *two* reasons why only some of the energy that was absorbed by plants
    was trapped and converted into biomass. (2 marks)

(b) Calculate how much energy (in $kJ\,m^{-2}\,yr^{-1}$) is available to the primary
    consumers in the stream. (1 mark)

The efficiency of energy transfer between trophic levels is calculated by comparing the energy available to a trophic level with the energy available to the next trophic level.

Between secondary and tertiary consumers, this is calculated as follows:

$$\frac{\text{energy available to tertiary consumers}}{\text{energy available to secondary consumers}} \times 100\%$$

(c) Use the formula above to calculate the efficiency of energy transfer between the secondary consumers and the tertiary consumers in Figure 1. Show your working and express your answer to the nearest whole number.   (2 marks)

(d) Explain how energy is lost between the consumer trophic levels in a community.   (4 marks)

Freshwater streams are examples of open ecosystems, because there is energy flow with other, neighbouring, ecosystems.

(e) Explain how the energy flow diagram in Figure 1 shows that the freshwater stream is an open ecosystem.   (3 marks)

Total: 12 marks

■ ■ ■

Candidates' answers to Question 7

Candidate A

(a) Not all the light hits chlorophyll molecules in chloroplasts. Some of the light energy is wasted because there is not enough carbon dioxide available for photosynthesis.

Candidate B

(a) Some light energy misses the leaves; some is reflected from the surface of the leaves.

    e Candidate A gives two good reasons why much of the light *absorbed* by the plant is not converted into energy in biomass. Candidate B has missed the point and gets no marks. Light that 'misses the leaves' is light that is not absorbed. This candidate has not read the question carefully. Similarly, reflected light is light that has not been absorbed. Plants are often unable to make use of the light they absorb because of limiting factors, such as low carbon dioxide concentration in the air and low temperatures. This is something you should remember from GCSE.

Candidate A

(b) $14\,147\,\text{kJ}\,\text{m}^{-2}\,\text{yr}^{-1}$

Candidate B

(b) 14 147

    e Candidate B has not given any units, but since they are in the question, this does not matter. However, it is good practice always to give the units in questions like this.

Candidate A

(c) $(95/1609) \times 100 = 6\%$

Candidate B

(c) 5.904%

e Candidate B has again failed to read the question and does not get any marks. The examiner has asked for the working to be shown and the answer to be given to the nearest whole number. Full marks are often given for the correct answer without any working, but it is good practice to give the working just in case you make a mistake with the final answer. Remember to take a calculator into the examination with you. There will almost always be questions like this. In your coursework, the importance of significant figures will have been emphasised. This is just as important in these papers. Do not simply copy all the numbers from your calculator (in this case 5.9042883). This is pointless — the examiner is helping you by asking for an answer 'to the nearest whole number'.

Candidate A

(d) Energy is not passed on because some energy is lost by the respiration of the secondary consumers. Some energy goes to decomposers in urine, faeces and dead bodies. The animals also lose energy as heat when they move around. A tertiary consumer does not eat all of the body of a secondary consumer (e.g. the bones are often left).

Candidate B

(d) Secondary consumers produce energy when they respire and much of this is lost to the air as heat. Some energy goes to decomposers. Secondary consumers do not eat all of the primary consumers.

e Candidate A has identified six reasons why the energy is not passed on. Candidate B has made the error of stating that 'energy is produced'. You should remember that energy is neither created nor destroyed; this means that it cannot be 'produced'. The candidate should refer to energy **transfer** in respiration or energy **conversion**. The candidate says that energy 'goes to decomposers', but does not explain how. The idea presented in the last sentence is correct. Candidate B gets 2 marks.

Candidate A

(e) Dead material, in this case dead leaves from surrounding trees, enters the stream from outside. This provides 2031 kJ m^2 yr^{-1}. Some materials leave the ecosystem (accounting for 10 500 kJ m^2 yr^{-1}), because they are washed downstream.

Candidate B

(e) The diagram shows that energy flows into and out of the ecosystem.

e There are 3 marks for this question. Candidate B has only given one point, for 1 mark, and has not referred to the information in the energy flow diagram. You will be expected to translate information from one form into another in the unit test. This question tests this skill.

e **Candidate B is awarded 4 marks out of 12 for this question.**

Overall, Candidate B scores 31 out of 91, which at 34% is unlikely to attain a grade E.